LITURGICAL
MUSIC INCUNABULA

LITURGICAL MUSIC INCUNABULA

A Descriptive Catalogue

BY

KATHI MEYER-BAER

LONDON
THE BIBLIOGRAPHICAL SOCIETY
1962

BIBLIOGRAPHICAL SOCIETY PUBLICATION
FOR THE YEAR 1954
ISSUED 1962

PREFACE

THIS catalogue of liturgical incunabula is the result of studies that go back to 1935. My interest in the subject began in the course of a visit of two professors to the Paul Hirsch Library at Frankfurt-am-Main. A Missale Wormatiense, printed by Wenssler at Basle, was out on an old lectern at the time. The missal had been dated, by an expert book dealer, 1488. The two professors, who were specialists in medieval music, but not experts in music printing, stated that the book had been printed *much* earlier.

My suspicions were aroused, however, and I set out to compare all Wenssler editions in German libraries, and to study the related documents. I found that the book dealer was right, and that Wenssler had printed music only in the one year 1488.

While working on Wenssler, I discovered that in most incunabula catalogues the manner of printing music was completely ignored, and I decided to fill the gap. I elaborated a method, and started with the books listed in the British Museum catalogue of incunabula printed in Italy, Germany, and Switzerland. My first descriptive list was published in *The Library* December 1939. From 1938 to 1940 I investigated the four great libraries in Paris, and found a rich treasure of books, many of them printed in France, which had hitherto not been known to contain printed music. The Bibliothèque Nationale agreed to print my list of these books. Unfortunately the war interrupted these plans, the head of the Bibliothèque Nationale being interned and my family leaving Europe for the United States. The French list was translated into English and was accepted for publication by the Bibliographical Society.

After the end of the war, the Secretary of the Society suggested that the two lists—the British Museum and the Paris lists—might be printed together as a single work. I felt that for publication as a book the survey should be enlarged, and items in the great libraries of Oxford and Cambridge, as well as those in American libraries, should be included. This project would not have been possible without the financial help of two organizations. The International Association of University Women granted me the Mary E. Woolley fellowship for my trip to Europe, and the American Council of Learned Societies granted me the means to complete my research in America by a trip to the South-West, to Austin, Texas, and to the West, to the Huntington Library in Pasadena, California. It has thus been possible to describe books in the following libraries: Bibliothèque Nationale, Bibliothèque de l'Arsenal, Bibliothèque Mazarine, and Bibliothèque Ste-Geneviève in Paris, the British Museum, the Bodleian Library, the Cambridge University Library, and American libraries.

The survey would have been more complete had I included *all* French and *all* English libraries. The chief reason that led me to postpone this task to a later date was that there are no complete printed surveys of incunabula in England or in France.

Preface

To all who have helped me in my work I extend my sincerest thanks. Dr. Curt Bühler, of the Pierpont Morgan Library, New York, who read the book in proof, has offered many valuable suggestions. The typographical problems implicit in the printing of a catalogue of this nature have been solved with exemplary care by the Oxford University Press. I also acknowledge my indebtness to all previous bibliographies, catalogues, and monographs on liturgical incunabula. Though I have frequently had to correct statements given in them, my work would have been impossible without their help. To the two organizations, the International Association of University Women and the American Council of Learned Societies, go my warmest feelings of gratitude for having enabled me to finish my studies.

New Rochelle, N.Y., 1961

CONTENTS

ILLUSTRATIONS

following page xliv

INTRODUCTION

WHILE there are bibliographies of incunabula which deal with the theory of music,[1] there are no bibliographies of those which contain actual music. These are, with few, possibly three or four, exceptions, liturgical books.

The music in liturgical incunabula is Gregorian chant. The tunes were assembled in three different ways: 1. following the festivals of the year, the so-called *cursus*. The collections designed for the celebration of the Mass are the Missal and the Gradual; those for the prayer service of the Hours or *officia* are the *Antiphonarium* and the *Responsoriale*; 2. collections of the melodies sung during processions and used in special services such as funeral rites, baptism, &c. The general title for this group is Ritual; 3. collections of liturgical poetry in special forms, e.g. the hymns and the sequences, and the Psalter.

This catalogue contains descriptions of the printed music in liturgical incunabula in the great libraries in England and France, and the United States. It seeks to compare the different methods of printing music and to define the different styles, thus providing new means for identifying single leaves and determining variants of so-called 'editions'.

By way of introduction I have discussed in the following sections some of the main features of the subject.

1. THE SERVICE BOOKS

A. *Books for the Mass*

Missals are the books containing those parts of the liturgy of the Mass which are recited *and* sung by the priest, and that are recited only by the choir. Their order follows the *cursus* beginning with the First Sunday in Advent. Usually the Missal is prefaced by a calendar listing the names of the festivals. By using this calendar we are often able to identify a Missal as belonging to a certain diocese, especially if festivals peculiar to a certain cathedral or to a particular saint are listed. Sometimes a Missal begins with a special service for the dedication of a church or a rite connected with it, as the sanctification of the house. Normally, however, it starts with the antiphon: *Ad te levavi*, the opening antiphon of the Introit of the First Sunday in Advent.

Just as in modern Missals, the *Ordinarium Missae*[2] was inserted in the *Proprium de Tempore*, and in the middle of the *Ordinarium* the *Canon Missae*. To emphasize the importance of the *Canon* a different and larger-sized type was used; in most editions the lines occupy the full width of the printed page, whereas the remainder of the book was printed in two columns. Sometimes the *Canon* was the

---

[1] Bibl. 54.

[2] The terms *Ordinarium* and *Commune* refer to the parts which are repeated daily; the term *Proprium* refers to the variable parts.

only part of the Missal printed on vellum, and the *Te igitur* was usually given a special decorative capital 'T'. Very often the leaf before the *Canon* had a picture with a representation of the Crucifixion. If music was printed in the part before the *Canon*, the method of setting was usually different from that in the later sections. Thus the music before the *Canon* was printed in two columns, while in the *Canon* it occupied the whole width of the page. Frequently also the number of the staves on a page was greater in the part before the *Canon*. The melody of the *Pater Noster* was usually given in the *Canon*.

A large number of the Missals follow the use established for the diocese of Rome. Among the 459 Missals listed for the fifteenth century by Weale[1] no fewer than 121 are Roman Missals. In these the printing is arranged in a manner similar to that used in modern books. There may be music only in the part before the *Canon*; in the part before *and* in the *Canon*; and in some Missals there is also music in the part after the *Canon*. The majority had music before the *Canon* only, and it was sometimes inserted in a single quire consisting of from sixteen to thirty leaves devoted solely to this purpose.

Missals published for certain dioceses, usually stating in the title the name of the town for which they were compiled, have slight differences in the melodies and include special Masses for festivals of local saints. The characterization of a service in the calendar as *simplex* or *duplex* indicates the importance of the feast; thus, the festival of a local saint was always a double one in its town, and in a local Missal the appropriate melodies had to be printed, while in an ordinary Missal they could be omitted. Such special festivals are listed either in the index, if one is printed at the beginning or the end of the book, or in the calendar. If, for example, on 9 September the special festival of the dedication *ecclesiae Constantiensis* is listed, we can confidently presume that the Missal was printed for the diocese of Constance.

A third group of Missals was published for certain ecclesiastical orders. Here the arrangement of the liturgy and the melodies varies considerably. This can be recognized from the fact that in these Missals often only the staves are printed, not the musical notes. The *Missalia Ordinis Praedicatorum* are exceptional in this respect. Of the thirty-seven Missals for monastic orders which Weale lists, twenty-one appear in our list; six of these do not contain music; eight have staves or space left for them; seven print actual music. Five Missals of this latter group were published for the *Ordo Praedicatorum*.

Missalia specialia, books containing Masses for special purposes, as for peace, for charity, &c., or for certain occasions, such as the victory over the Turks in 1492, form a fourth group. The titles of these books do not always indicate their special character. The *Missale Lausannense* (Weale 492) is an example, as well as all the *Missalia Itinerantium*. No book of this kind with music, however, is known to the compiler of this catalogue, though the catalogue of the Brussels Library mentions a *Missale speciale votivale* with 'espaces réservées pour la notation du plain chant'.[2]

---

[1] Bibl. 51.   [2] Bibl. 41.

Other *Missalia specialia* contain the liturgies of the *cursus* in addition to the special Masses, but they usually emphasize the special Masses by placing them first. The term *speciale* may also indicate a local version as in the *Missale Speciale Herbipolense* (Weale 434).

Of the 459 fifteenth-century Missals listed by Weale, 226 items are included in our list. One hundred of them have actual music printed, while thirty-three have no indication of music whatsoever. The rest either have staves printed without melodies, or have spaces in which staves can be printed or drawn. When there is printed music it is usually to be found in the section before the *Canon*; sometimes a whole quire containing music is inserted directly before the *Canon*, or, less frequently, at the end of the book. When this section stands before the *Canon*, the numbering of the leaves continues through the gathering with music. Sometimes the numbers are printed, sometimes omitted. If the text type of the gathering with music is the same as that used in the rest of the book, we may presume that all the printing was done at the same press. In one or two cases we may conclude that the printed music was added later, in a different town and at another press. This question will be discussed later when speaking of the technical problems.

The Gradual contains the melodies of the service of the Mass sung by the choir. The number of printed Graduals is small, compared with the number of Missals. In comparison with 459 Missals listed by Weale, Bohatta[1] lists only eight Graduals, to which one more can be added. All printed Graduals of the fifteenth century contain music throughout. The order of the Graduals, as of the Missals, follows the *cursus*; it, too, begins with the introit of the First Sunday *Ad te levavi*. The Gradual does not include the *Canon*.

The most interesting Gradual in the catalogue is that in the British Museum, IB 6883 (no. 15). It is printed with the type used in the Constance Breviary dated 'not after 1473', and, on the basis of the watermarks, has been ascribed to the press of Guenther Zainer at Augsburg. It may be the earliest known example of music printed with type throughout a whole book.

B. *The Service Books for the Hours*

The most important of these is the *Antiphonarium* or *Antiphonale*. The title is related to the manner of chanting by alternating choirs: the monks whose chief duty was the performance of this service formed two facing groups; each section having a leader, a *cantor*, and an assistant *cantor*. The Antiphonary starts with the versicle *Domine, labia mea aperies*. It contains all the melodies for the prayer service, both those sung by the choir and those sung by the *cantor*. The parts for the choir alone are contained in the *Responsoriale* (or what is today called the *Vesperale*). There are six fifteenth-century Antiphonaries extant, all of them containing printed music throughout the book. There is only one item (No. 253) to which the title *Responsoriale* can be applied; this gives the printed melodies of the responses sung by the choir in the funeral service.

---

[1] Bibl. 3.

Books of Hours, as well as Breviaries, are used for the same sections of the service as the Antiphonary, but both were meant for private use, to be read rather than to be sung aloud; thus in the printed Books of Hours and Breviaries we do not find music.

The series of Hours for one day, celebrating the memory of a saint or a special festival, is called *officium*. The *officium* is the most important cyclical form of liturgical poetry from the sixth century on, and finally became the basis of the musical form of oratorio. Several such offices are found in the Antiphonary, and also in the Processionaries. No complete separately published *officium* with printed music is known from the incunabula period; books with the title *officium* or *officia* are actually Psalters or Books of Hours, or parts of them. *Officiale* is an alternative title for the *Ordinarium* or the *Directorium*.

The *officium* concludes with the story of the saint or martyr. This legend or *historia* was sung; one such item printed before 1500, the *Historia S. Leopoldi* (no. 21), is still extant. Under the title *Historia* we normally find stories in prose rather than liturgical texts; the *Legenda Aurea* is the best-known collection.

C. *Books of Shortened Form*

In all the books we have described so far, the texts and the melodies, where they are given, are printed in full. There are other kinds of books for the same parts of the liturgy which give only the order and the incipits of the texts: the *Ordinaria* and *Directoria* for the liturgy of the Mass, and the *Collectaria* for the service of the Hours. These titles are very general, and they are very vague and uncertain guides. The meaning of the term directory has greatly changed through the years. For example, in the seventeenth century a directory was primarily a textbook for the conductor of a choir. The liturgical directory starts, like the Missal, with a calendar in which the days of the weeks are marked with the letters a–g; the calendar also indicates whether a festival is *simplex* or *duplex*. The magnitude of the feast regulates the number of antiphons and versicles to be sung. Some of the directories give only this information. A complete directory lists also the incipits and the order of the antiphons to be sung. The *Ordinaria*—not to be confused with the *Ordinarium Missae*—add the indication of the liturgical duties of the clerics, such as genuflexion, &c. These books are the equivalent in print of the manuscript *libri officii* or *Amtsbücher* which in their turn are an important source for the music in medieval monasteries. Among the *Directoria* and *Collectaria*[1] no book with music could be found, but an *Ordinarium Praemonstratense* (nos. 228a and 228b) has space left in some chapters for music to be added. That music was intended to be inserted into the spaces must be assumed since the text underneath is obviously spaced out to correspond with the musical notation.

D. *Books for Special Services*

The uncertainty and variety of the titles of the books in this group are a major problem. In our list they appear under such titles as *Agenda, Baptesimale,*

---

[1] One printed *Collectarium* only is extant.

Benedictionale, Ceremoniale, Exequiale, Liber Catechumeni, Litaniae, Manuale, Obsequiale, Pontificale, Processionarium, Regulae, and *Vigiliae.* The *Pontificale* was used in cathedrals where a bishop was officiating. *Litaniae* are part of a *Processionarium* and were sometimes printed separately. The custom of printing separate parts and often in a varying order has made the task of identifying books in this group very difficult. A further complication is caused by the tradition of using double titles, such as *Ceremoniale vel Obsequiale.* The term *Rituale* has at times been used as a common denominator; but this has not been universally accepted, nor has it been consistently observed. The *Gesamtkatalog,* for instance, apparently intended to put all these books under the heading *Rituale;* nevertheless, there is a separate heading for the *Agenda,* actually the most common of the Rituals. No. 254 of our list is referred to as a *Rituale* in the reference books; neither of the copies, in the British Museum and in the Huntington Library, however, has a title, and the contents are identical with those of an *Agenda,* or more specifically with a *Liber Catechumeni.* The index lists the following rites:

> Ad catechumenum faciendum
> Ad baptizandum puerum vel puellam
> Ad purificandum mulierem post partum
> Missa pro sponso et sponsa
> Ad communicandum infirmum
> Ad recommendandum animam eiusdem
> Ad sepeliendum funus
> Ad sepeliendum pueros in ecclesia
> Ad tondendos capillos puerorum
> Ad benedicendum aquam
> > sportas et baculos
> > domum
> > panem et vinum
> > ova et caseum
> > carnes
> > poma
> > omnia quae volueris

As the *Baptesimale* and *Liber Catechumeni* place special emphasis on the rites of baptism, and as our No. 254 starts with these rites, it might be better listed under *Baptesimale. Benedictionale* and *Ceremoniale* are practically the same as the *Agenda. Exequiale* and *Obsequiale* emphasize the funeral rites. In the books with the title *Vigiliae* we find melodies for the funeral service only. These books are similar to the *Obsequiale.* There are, however, *Vigiliae* which are similar to the *Livres d'Heures* with French rubrics and no melodies.

Manuale is a title used for various compilations. There are *Manualia* which are selections of *Missae votivae;* that is, they are *Missalia Specialia,* more or less following the *cursus.* Often the title indicates the locality for which the *Manuale* was published. French editions of this kind have printed music; German editions have space left, and Spanish Manuals are not intended for any music.

There are other *Manualia sive Instructoria* which are similar to the *Agenda*. All bibliographies of liturgical books include the *Manuale Parochialium Sacerdotum*. This, however, is not a liturgical book at all; it is connected with the liturgy only in so far as it gives a theoretical explanation of the sacraments.

Identification is often difficult because these books, or parts of them, are often bound in different orders. To give one example: the *Ceremoniale Bursfeldense* in the British Museum was originally the second part of a volume, of which the first part was the *Ordinarium Bursfeldense*; the two parts were separated and catalogued separately under different titles and numbers. In the earlier bibliographies the part entitled *Ceremoniale* is not mentioned. In his *Bibliographia liturgica* Weale lists the two parts together as a Missal (no. 1679). A copy in the Bibliothèque Nationale has the order: *Martyrologium, Ceremoniale, Ordinarium*, and is to be found under the heading *Martyrologium*.

Most of the books for special services contain printed music. They were published in many different places, even in places where no other liturgical printing was undertaken. The more important the cathedral for which such a book was published, the richer is the liturgy. The melodic versions in these books are identical, except in the case of the tunes in the Processionaries. Since folksongs were often sung during processions, it might prove worth while to compare their differences.

E. *Hymnals and Psalters*

There remain the books containing collections of liturgical poetry in special forms. These are the Hymnals, Sequentiaria or Sequentialia, and the Psalters. Very few of these can properly be considered liturgical books, since they are mostly designed for private devotion or as textbooks. Sometimes this is indicated in the title, which then reads 'with commentary', *cum commentario*, or *expositiones in . . .*; on the other hand, such information was often omitted. The size of a book will generally determine whether it was intended for liturgical use. Books in folio, such as the famous Psalters by Schoeffer, were meant for use in the church; books in pocket size were meant for private use. Many of the Psalters and Hymnals are nothing more than extracts from the Bible or the Diurnale, that part of the Breviary intended for the service during day-time. Such separate editions seldom have a title and never have music. The *Expositiones hymnorum et sequentiarum* are extant in numerous editions; some printers seem to have specialized in the printing of this book. No edition with music has yet been found.

The Psalters vary greatly in size and kind. We have Psalters that present the whole text of the psalms in numerical order, and those that arrange the verses of the psalms as they are used in the liturgy. We have Psalters that give only the psalms used for certain purposes, such as the penitential psalms for the funeral service. We have Psalters that do not contain the Latin text of the psalms but paraphrases or adaptations in Latin or in the vernaculars. We have Psalters that are extracts from the Bible or the Missal only, and Psalters bound together with certain *officia*. Such variety makes a bibliographical definition very difficult, and all information supplied by liturgical bibliographies remains vague. Bohatta[1] lists about 200 Latin Psalters (nos. 794–982). The actual number may be much smaller, since one and the same edition *sine nota* may be listed several times if owned by different libraries. Most of them were not intended for use in the liturgy and do not have printed music. Of the eighty-nine Psalters in the catalogue fourteen have space left for music, three have actual music printed. Thus approximately a fifth were designed to include music in one form or other—the opposite of our findings with the Missals, where only one-sixth did not have some musical significance.

2. RUBRICS

The rubrics may provide help in the identification of the sort of liturgical book to which a single leaf once belonged. If such a rubric provides only a general information such as antiphon or versicle, often the text of the antiphon will help. Modern editions of the Antiphonary (*Vesperale*) and the Gradual, as well as the earlier editions of Pustet, have useful indexes. Since, however, some fifteenth-century liturgies include melodies which were subsequently discarded or replaced, these will not, of course, appear in such indexes; in that event the *Repertorium* of Ulysse Chevalier[2] may be of help. Further information on these obsolete texts may be obtained from the Publications of the Plainsong and Medieval Society, the *Paléographie musicale*, and the *Paleografia Musicale Vaticana*, all of which contain detailed and reliable indexes.

3. METHOD OF DESCRIPTION

This list contains about 800 items. Of these the compiler has been able to examine approximately 450, or rather more than half. As this catalogue is concerned chiefly with the printing of the music, no attempt has been made to attribute undetermined books to particular presses; question marks have been added only where an attribution seemed very doubtful. Similarly an examination of the different versions of the melodies has not been considered essential. Such a study would have to be based on books with manuscript as well as printed music. The purpose of the present book is to define and compare the different techniques and styles of printing, and to mark variants in so-called 'identical' editions.

Initially the compiler hoped to be able to describe the printed music in such detail and so accurately that any portion and fragment could henceforth be identified with certainty. In the course of compilation, however, problems arose which have tempered this optimistic view. On the whole, however, the results are believed to be founded on safe premisses.

In any description of printed music in fifteenth-century books we should expect to find the answers to the following questions, which have been divided into four groups and set down in tabular form:

[1] Bibl. 3.   [2] Bibl. 9.

Introduction

A. What parts of the music are printed, and in what sections of the book?

  1. Are there printed staves and printed notes?

  2. Are the staves printed and the notes in manuscript?

  3. Are only the staves printed?

  4. Has space been left for staves and notes?

  5. Is there no space left for the music?

  6. In what parts of the book do we find music?

B. The form of the notes.

  1. Is the form of the notes roman?

  1*a.* Does this roman form imitate neumes?

  2. Is the form of the notes gothic?

  3. Do ligatures occur, and in what particular design?

  4. Are the ligatures broken up into single notes?

  5. Are the outlines of a single note straight or curved, and do these outlines have little points at the corners?

  6. Has the single note a stem?

C. The staves and the borderlines of a page.

  1. Are the staves set in one or two columns?

  2. How many staves are there to a page?

  3. How many lines does a stave have?

  4. Are the staves printed in red or black?

  5. Are there staves only, without a border round the page?

  6. If there is a border,

    (*a*) does the border occur at the sides only?

    (*b*) does the border occur at the top and the bottom only?

    (*c*) does the border go all round?

    (*d*) is the border made up of one line or two?

  7. Are the staves

    (*a*) printed from several pieces for the width of a column?

    (*b*) printed from one single piece for the width of a column?

    (*c*) set with single or double metal rules?

D. 1. What is the form of the clefs?

  2. What is the form of the catchnotes or guides?

  3. Are there red or black vertical bars in the staves to separate words or sentences?

  4. Other remarks.

The reason for dividing up the information in this way will be readily understood after a consideration of the groups themselves. The grouping was arrived at empirically during the course of the work. It was first applied to the liturgical books printed by Wenssler,[1] then, in supplemented form, to the books in the British Museum.[2] In this list it has again been supplemented. It has seemed helpful to describe the form of the single note; and further, a third style of notes,

---

[1] Bibl. 36.   [2] Bibl. 34.

similar to the roman, but imitating the old handwritten neumes, has had to be added.

The word 'raster', which was previously used to describe one way of producing the staves, has had to be replaced. The 'raster', a fivefold pen, might have been used to design the lines of the staves on the material of the type, and the solid material—wood or metal—might have been chiselled out between the lines drawn by the raster. But this tool was not applied directly to the paper or vellum, unless the music was handwritten.

4. THE CHIEF FORMS OF MUSICAL SYMBOLS

The music in printed liturgical books is always plain or Gregorian chant. The music is unisono, and the rhythm of a melody is directed by the rhythm of the text. Thus, the notes do not show any rhythmical differences. On the other hand, the exact pitch of a note is always determined through its position on the stave.

The basic form of the single note is called virga or punctum, depending on whether the note has a stem or not. The single note can be printed in roman or gothic style. The former style is favoured in Latin, the latter in German countries.[1] A few printers, like Hopyl, used both styles. The forms of the notes were modelled on those in the manuscripts.[2] In the forms of the roman note we can distinguish between straight ▫ or curved ◘ ◘ outlines, between notes with, ⊓ ⊐, or without, points, ▫. Some printers use the punctum only, some the virga only. Some use both, and some take a virga to designate the beginning or end of a word or sentence.

Punctum	Roman ▫	Gothic ◇
Virga	¶ ₧ ♩ ♭	⇑ ⇑

A hook on a single note designates a *nota liquescens*, that is a kind of trill or grace in the liturgical chant. Besides the single note, there are ligatures, where several notes are bound (*ligatae*) together to indicate that they correspond to one word or syllable. Sometimes these ligatures have very typical forms and can help to identify a printer. Most common are the ligatures for two notes. The ascending one is called Podatus, the descending one Clivis. The same combination can be used for different and wider intervals.

Podatus	Roman ♬ ⅃	Gothic ⬦ ◦⇑
Clivis	♭ Ɛ	⋔ ⋈ ⇑◦

The ligatures for three notes are: Scandicus or Salicus for three ascending notes, Climacus for three descending notes, Torculus with a higher note in the middle, and Porrectus with a lower note in the middle.

Scandicus	Roman ♫	Gothic ◦◦⇑ ◦⬦
Climacus	♯♭	⋈◦ ⇑◦

---

[1] Bibl. 38, 53.   [2] The roman form is still used in the modern liturgical books.

Torculus	Roman 🜩	Gothic ⌇ ◦⌇
Porrectus	🜪	⇑ ⚬

Apart from the single note and the ligatures the guides or catchnotes are important symbols. The catchnote stands at the end of a line, and in the place where the music of the next line begins. The printing of catchnotes is not usual in modern books.

The forms of the clefs, too, can be an important help in the identification of printers. They are developed from the single note or from letters. The C- and the F-clef were generally used; the G-clef, today in use as the so-called violin clef, was used by only one printer, Ratdolt, in the *Antiphonarium* (no. 9) and the *Graduale* (no. 17). Nowadays for the F- or bass clef we use the form $\mathcal{9}$:; a somewhat related form, $\mathcal{9}$, was used in the incunabula period. The modern C-clef, used for alto or tenor parts (violoncello), was $\Vert\mathsf{H}\vert$; it was used in manuscripts, but not by printers of the fifteenth century. Some printers use both C- and F-clef at the same time, placed one beneath the other. The position of the clefs varies, that is, the clef is put on the line where it is most needed.

The reason why the old editions have four lines only for the stave is because the compass of a melody was usually smaller, and did not need more than four lines and four spaces in the stave. Modern missals also have staves with four lines only. If the compass of a melody was wider, the clef would be moved to another line, gaining thereby an interval of a third or a fifth. In liturgical books there was relatively seldom a change of clef within a line because the width of a column was short, and because the compass of liturgical melodies, with the exception of the graduals, was narrow.

Table of the Forms of the Single and the Double Note and other Ligatures, of the Clefs and Catchnotes, as used by the Printers of the Incunabula Period

Single note gothic	𝄞	Ratdolt
	◦ ⟩ ⟫	Grueninger Schoeffer
	⌇	*Graduale Constantiense*
	𝄽	Hopyl
	⇑	Petri
	⇑ ⟋	Pruess
	⇑ ◦	Petri Reyser[1]
	⏐ ⏐ ◦ 𝄾	Reyser Stuchs
	⏐ ◦ 𝄾	Drach Wenssler
Single note roman	⟋	Pruess Sensenschmidt Wenssler
	⟩	Higman Hopyl
	⌓	Higman Pynson Sachon
	⊓ ⟋	Hamman
	⊣	Arndes Hamman
	⊣	Comp. Alemanes Ungut *Missale Sarum*

[1] If not indicated otherwise Reyser stands for Georg Reyser.

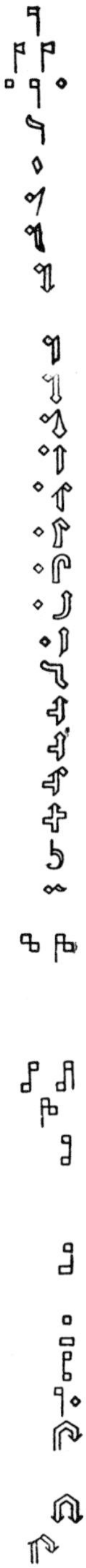

	Hamman Sessa Tortis
	Spira
	Higman Morin
	Benaliis
	Higman Pynson
Single note similar to neumes	Pachel Valdarfer
Double note gothic	Schoeffer
	Graduale Constantiense Kachelofen Ratdolt Reyser Richel Sensenschmidt Stuchs Wenssler
	Petri Ratdolt Stuchs
	Sensenschmidt
	Pfeyl
	Stuchs
	Ratdolt Reyser
	Ratdolt
	Reyser Sensenschmidt
	Drach
	Drach Ratdolt
	M. Reyser
	Wenssler Pruess
	Psalterium, Mainz
	Schoeffer
	Graduale Constantiense
Double note similar to neumes	*Missale Sarum*
	Valdarfer
Double note roman	Arndes Arrivabene Boninis Dupré Fratres Eremiti Gering Hamman Han Higman Hodian Morand Regnault Scotus Sessa Spira Ungut
	Comp. Alemanes Spira
	Planck
	Boninis Fratres Eremiti Han Higman Maréchal Morand Paganinis Planck Regnault Sachon Spira
	Arndes Bevilaqua Boninis Hamman Pachel Scotus Sessa Spira *Missale Tarentasie*
	Benaliis
	Dupré
	Luschner
Ligatures gothic	Drach Petri Pfeyl Pruess Ratdolt Reyser Schoeffer Stuchs Wenssler
	Ratdolt
	Hamman/Petri Pfeyl *Psalterium* No. 244 Ratdolt Reyser Richel

Ligatures gothic (*contd.*):   Pruess

Ratdolt

Petri   Stuchs

Graduale Constantiense

Higman/Hopyl   Sensenschmidt

Wenssler   *Psalterium* No. 244

Reyser

Ligatures roman   *Missale Sarum*

Arrivabene   Bevilaqua   Hamman   Novimagio Sessa   Spira   Torresanus   Tortis (?)   Ungut Boninis

Britannicis   Benaliis

Valdarfer

Spira

Arrivabene   Bevilaqua   Hamman   Sessa   Spira

Arndes   Gering   Hopyl   Morand   Morin Maréchal

Le Blanc   Spira   Gering   Numeister/Topié Bevilaqua

Novimagio   Benaliis   Luschner

Valdarfer

Le Blanc

Boninis   Dupré   Higman   Hodian   Hopyl Morand   Pynson   Spira

Gering   Higman

Morand   Pynson

Arndes

Gering (*Psalterium*)   Olivier

Luschner

Spira

Arndes

Ungut

Olivier   Luschner   Spira

Spira (Giunta?)

Catchnotes   Sensenschmidt

Arrivabene   Benaliis   Bevilaqua   Boninis   Britannicis   Drach   Hamman   Han   Hopyl Kachelofen   Maréchal   Numeister   Pachel   Petri Pfeyl   Planck   M. Reyser   Ratdolt   Sachon Sessa   Spira (Giunta?)   Stuchs   Topié   Torresanus   Ungut   Wenssler   *Psalterium* No. 244

Arrivabene

Pruess

de Odis

	⌐	Comp. Alemanes
		Boninis
		Novimagio Zarotus
		Spira Tortis Wenssler
		Gering Higman Morin Olivier
		Ratdolt Richel Pruess
		Pachel Valdarfer
		Giunta (?) Hamman Pachel Ratdolt Schoeffer Tortis (?)
		Ratdolt Luschner
		Ratdolt
		Ratdolt Girardengus
		Le Blanc
		Psalterium No. 249
		Pynson
		Graduale Constantiense
		Missale Sarum
Clefs	Double	Drach
		Sensenschmidt Pfeyl
		Higman/Hopyl
	C	Reyser Richel Wenssler
		Wenssler
		Ratdolt
		Arrivabene Hamman Ratdolt Reyser Sachon Spira Torresanus
		Pfeyl
		M. Reyser
		Reyser
		Sensenschmidt
		Graduale Constantiense Hamman Petri Ratdolt Sensenschmidt
		Hamman
		Wenssler Stuchs
		Drach *Psalterium* No. 244
		Kachelofen Stuchs
		Stuchs
		Pachel
		Maréchal Novimagio Spira
		Benaliis Boninis Britannicis Fratres Eremiti Hamman Han Higman Girardengus Le Blanc Morin Olivier de Odis Planck Scotus Spira

Clefs C (*contd*):

                Missale Tarentasie Valdarfer

         Arrivabene Tortis

         Arndes Boninis Dupré Gering Higman Hodian Hopyl Luschner Maynial Morand Planck Pachel Pynson Regnault Spira Ungut Zarotus

         Benaliis Spira

         Paganinis

         Sessa

         Numeister Topié

         Comp. Alemanes

F   Reyser Pfeyl Schoeffer

         Sensenschmidt

         M. Reyser

         Pynson

         Drach Petri Pruess Ratdolt Richel Wenssler

         Pfeyl Sensenschmidt Stuchs

         Ratdolt Sensenschmidt Stuchs

         Hamman/Petri

         Stuchs

         Graduale Constantiense

         Missale Sarum

         Pruess (?)

         Grueninger Schoeffer

         Ratdolt

         Arrivabene Bevilaqua Hamman Novimagio Spira Tortis

         Sessa

         Britannicis Hamman Scotus (very small)

         Missale Tarentasie

         Benaliis Boninis Britannicis Hamman Maréchal Scotus Sessa Spira

         de Odis

         Bevilaqua

         Paganinis

         Fratres Eremiti

         Comp. Alemanes

         Luschner

         Arndes

         Bevilaqua Sessa Spira

         Sessa

         Pynson

         Tortis (?) Spira (?)

         Hamman Spira Torresanus

ꟼ⌗ ꟼ⌗	Girardengus				
◇⌗	Spira				
◌◔ ꟼ◌	Pachel				
ꟼ⌗	Dupré	Gering	Higman	Hodian	Hopyl
	Morand	Morin	(Olivier)	Pynson	Regnault
ꟼ⌗	Gering				
⌗ꟼ	Le Blanc	Maynial	Pynson		
ꟼ⌗	Numeister				
⅏	Ratdolt				

G

5. THE PRINTING

The two questions most frequently asked in reference to the printing of music are: (1) Why is music sometimes printed from woodblock and sometimes from type? Does this represent the difference between an earlier and a more developed technique? and (2) Why are only the staves printed in some books? Does this mean that people learned first to print staves, and only later to add the notes? Can we distinguish two periods of proficiency? The answers to these two questions become clear in a consideration of the technique of the printing of music.

Other questions also arise: (1) Who were the actual printers of music? (2) Are there variations in the setting of music in different copies of one edition, and if so, why? (3) How does this affect the problem of 'one' edition, and the reliability of our conclusions?

The printer's main task was to arrange the plainchant melodies to correspond (on the page) with the liturgical text. How he solved this task depended, of course, on the purpose for which the book was published. It was this rather than any degree of proficiency which determined the kind of printing.

A. *Woodblock or Type*

It has been thought that printing from woodblocks represents an earlier and simpler technique than printing from type. This assumption is true in only a very restricted sense. There is printing from woodblocks in most of the incunabula on the theory of music and there is printing from type in almost all the liturgical incunabula. There is also printing from type in the only known example of a work containing secular music with measured notes from this period.[1]

Whether woodblock or type was used depended mainly on the contents of the book. Books on the theory of music were mostly textbooks for schools and universities, the contents of which hardly differed from edition to edition, or from author to author; even illustrations could often be interchanged. Consider the 'Guidonian hand', for example. A woodcut representation of it might be

[1] Bibl. 35.

used in different treatises and in different chapters. The text would vary some-what, just as it does in modern textbooks, but an illustration might stay un-altered. Thus one woodblock could be used several times in one book and in any number of books.

The contents of the liturgical books were also stable. Open a manuscript Missal of a thousand years ago and you will find the same text as today; but we do not find the same musical notation. This was still developing during our period. Besides, the melodies and the liturgies in different dioceses were not standard-ized. It was exceptional if the setting of the melody of one antiphon could be taken over from one edition to another. Thus we have many books for local use. Even if such an edition could be used only in a geographically restricted area, its printing was, nevertheless, worth while because it was intended to last over a long period, in contrast to textbooks which were quickly torn and worn out.

The second half of the fifteenth century coincided with a period in the de-velopment of measured music when it became so popular that it was taught in schools. Textbooks for this new art had to be produced, and the illustrations in them needed notes with measured, that is with different, rhythmical values. The use of many different forms for the notes complicated the cutting of the founts, and made the printing expensive. Publishers, therefore, tried to use one example in as many editions as possible; this was easier to do from a woodblock. On the other hand, the melodies in the liturgical books were all plainchant, for which the printer needed only a limited number of sorts. This is probably the chief reason why type was used for printing liturgical books.

Actually in only two of the books in our list can it be said that the music was definitely printed from woodblocks. Molitor,[1] the foremost scholar in this field, mentions four books in all in which he presumes this technique was employed. Among these four are the Gothic *Obsequiale* by Ratdolt (No. 222) and the *Missale Romanum* (No. 150) in Roman style. The *Ordo infirmum inunguendi* of the City Library in Mainz, which is a separate section from an *Agenda*, probably printed after 1500, includes a small illustration with music, and belongs, as far as printing technique is concerned, to the group of textbooks. In the *Agenda Moguntinensis* (No. 5) it is possible that the actual notes are printed from woodblock, but definitely not the clefs or the catchnotes.

Thus, among the books containing printed music in our list, two were printed from woodblocks, and one was possibly printed in part in this way. Among the books on the theory of music, the balance is the other way. Only three books with printing from type are known: the example in Gerson's *Super Magnificat* printed by Fyner in Esslingen, 1473, so far still the earliest item with music printed from type, but here the notes only, not the staves, were printed; the example in Niger's *Grammatica brevis*, 1480, and the musical illustrations in Guerson's treatise on music printed by Michel de Toulouze, about 1496.[2]

It has next to be made clear what we mean when we speak of printing with type. In music printing this term, in particular the German word *Typendruck*, is

[1] Bibl. 38.   [2] Bibl. 35, 37.

normally used for the method that was introduced in the eighteenth century by Fournier and Breitkopf, but had been invented, or at least largely used, in France in the sixteenth and seventeenth centuries by publishers such as Haultin and Ballard.[1] In it the head and the stem of the note *and* the small part of the corresponding stave are cast together as a single sort. The technique found in liturgical incunabula is quite different: it is a double process, the staves generally being printed first, and then the notes. The expression 'printing with type' is used simply to mean that the notes were printed from type, and not from one block.

The notes were always printed in black, the staves almost always in red. Only three items in the list have the staves printed in black. Generally speaking, the printing was a twofold or threefold procedure. The text was usually printed with the notes and with the vertical strokes; the staves were printed with the initials and the rubrics. Where the initials and the staves were not printed by the same pull of the press the colour of their red differs. The so-called 'Congreve' technique,[2] whereby printing in red and black was performed in one impression, could be applied only when the spaces for the red and black parts did not coincide, as they do in the cases of notes and staves.

Many books have vertical bars, usually black, going across the staves, similar to modern barlines. In liturgical incunabula they were used to separate the musical phrase belonging to one word or one sentence of the text from another. Molitor[3] describes a book in which the staves only are printed, but which still has the vertical bars. This would suggest that the printer used the bars to distribute his notes to correspond with the text. Usually the bars are weak and shaky and seem to have been printed with thin metal rules. If we assume a threefold procedure of printing, the vertical bars were probably printed with the text, followed by the staves and the initials together, and then the notes. This seems to have been the usual order. In a few exceptional cases, as in the *Agenda Moguntinensis* (No. 5), we have to assume a separate printing of the notes and of the clefs and catchnotes. But this technique does not seem to have been normal.

B. *The Form of the Staves*

For the printer the setting of the staves seems to have been a greater problem than the printing of the notes. Actually in the very first attempts to print music with type, in the *Super Magnificat* by Fyner in Esslingen, and in the *Grammatica brevis* of Niger, the notes are printed from type, and the lines added in manuscript. Thus it is quite inaccurate to speak of an earlier period when printers could set the staves only, and of a later period when they had mastered the technique of printing both notes and staves.

The early printers seem to have used three different methods of printing the staves:

1. By setting several pieces of type side by side to fill the width of a column. This technique can be recognized by small vertical breaks occurring in all lines

---

[1] Bibl. 2.   [2] Bibl. 20.   [3] Bibl. 38.

of the stave at the same spot. Usually we find that three or four pieces of type occupy the full width of a column. The lengths of the separate pieces may be equal or they may differ.

2. By using *one* piece of type only for the whole width of the column. Whether this is of wood or metal is not easy to determine. The lines in the staves are generally rather thick, and the colour is spread evenly, both characteristics which suggest wood; but the findings are not always conclusive.

The word 'raster' was previously used to describe this technique; but I have now replaced it with the phrase 'single type', though I am conscious that this is a rather colourless expression.

3. By metal rules. This technique is recognizable by the curves occurring often in two lines at the same spot. As these irregularities occur identically in two lines, the use of a kind of double rule is probable.

When several different colours are used for the lines in one stave, we can assume that the stave was drawn by hand. We can also tell that the lines are drawn by hand, if they are not of exactly the same length.

C. *Fitting Notes and Staves Together*

The two problems which the printer had to solve, when he had cut the type for the notes and the other symbols, were to print notes and staves so that they fitted accurately and to arrange for notes to correspond to the text. As regards the second of these two problems the printer had guidance from manuscript practice. Liturgical manuscripts had a long tradition, and were so well and exactly written that they could be used as models. In studying incunabula it is sometimes necessary to look carefully at the music to distinguish manuscript from printing. Examples of two printed editions can be found where the setting is so much alike—but not identical—that one edition must have been the model for the later edition, or both might have used the same manuscript as a model. For instance, the settings in the two Ambrosian Missals, one by Valdarfer and one by Pachel in Milan (Nos. 35, 36), are so much alike that a relationship cannot be doubted. We find such similarities also in the two *Missalia Ratisponensia* (Nos. 110, 111) published seven years apart in Bamberg by Sensenschmidt, and by Pfeyl and Petzensteiner.

The two difficulties in fitting text to music are that sometimes the text for a single note needs more space than the note; sometimes the music needs more space than the text. The latter is the case if the melody has musical ornaments to be sung corresponding to one word or syllable. These ornaments are a characteristic trait of plainchant and occur frequently.

To come now to the printing of the actual music. In the books we are considering, the melodies are either distributed throughout the whole book or printed separately and inserted, usually, before the Canon—if the book is a Missal—or at the end. The text in these separate parts is, as a rule, printed in the same type as the rest of the book and it is probable that the section with music was set in the same printing-house as the book, since the numbering of the leaves in this section is continuous with that of the rest of the book, or the inserted leaves are allowed for if they are not foliated. This music section could be used for several editions, especially if these were published only a few years apart.

While we may conclude that music and text were printed in the same house—and there is no reason to doubt it—it is quite possible that the craftsmen who set the music were brought in specially. In some cases it seems very likely that these 'foreigners' brought their music type and material with them. Claudin[1] mentions collaboration of this kind in the case of books other than liturgical. We know[2] that Valdarfer, while working in Basle, obtained a set from Richel, and used it later in his own shop. In one instance, in the Utrecht Missal (No. 194), the colophon mentions the collaboration of the two printing-houses of Higman and Hopyl. There are other possibilities. The beautiful and justly famous Wenssler music type is also found in the books of other houses: in Strasbourg at Grüninger's, later in Mainz at Schoeffer's, and in an anonymous Psalter (Nos. 74, 243, and 244). The forms in use in Strasbourg appear to be identical with Wenssler's; in Mainz they appear to be slightly bigger and clumsier than Wenssler's, but apparently cut after his model. A comparison of the two founts, side by side, would reveal whether they are of the same size. In these cases it is not certain that the later printer bought Wenssler's music founts, though this might have happened. It is also possible that the craftsman who did the music printing for Wenssler–Kilchen bought the type and worked as a travelling printer. Failing documentary evidence, in itself most unlikely, it is impossible to assess the degree of co-operation between shop and shop.

Besides this kind of travelling printer which we suggest, we know of the famous travelling printers such as Boninis, Hus, and Numeister who signed their books. Wenssler on the other hand did not print music in his liturgical books after he had left Basle.

There is another fact which suggests that special craftsmen were employed for the setting of music—and that they might have brought with them their sets of type material. In some of the books where printed music occurs throughout, it is possible to distinguish different styles in different sections—just as we find different 'hands' in manuscripts. Thus in the Psalter by Gering (No. 248) different styles are discernible in the two sections with printed music: one printer uses numerous ligatures, while in the other section most ligatures are dissolved into single notes. The form of the notes and ligatures is otherwise the same in the two parts. In the *Missale Hildensemense* by Stuchs (No. 79, copy in the British Museum) there are four music sections, employing different forms. In sections 1 and 3 and 2 and 4, the single notes and the clefs are as follows:

Sections 1 and 3   ;

Sections 2 and 4   .

In another copy of the Missal at Williams College (No. 80), there are two sections with music; these are identical in style with the second section in the British

---

[1] Bibl. 10, 11.   [2] Bibl. 5.

Museum copy. The accompanying text is set by Stuchs with the same type throughout. It is thus clear that, for the setting of music, not only different craftsmen but also different sets of type might be employed.

D. *Variants of One Edition*

Variants occur in the setting of the music in different copies of the same edition. For these variants the term *Parallelausgaben* has been used;[1] but are these not rather variants of *one* edition? In a number of instances where it is possible to compare several copies of the same book, we find differences in the settings of music, while the texts are identical.

The variants can be of different kinds:

1. One section may be identical and another different. I have already mentioned the *Missale Hildensemense* (Nos. 79 and 80). Another case is the *Missale Basiliense* by Wenssler (No. 44): the copy of this book in the Augsburg City Library has space left for music in the part before the Canon only; the copy in the Huntington Library has space left in the parts both before and after the Canon (fols. 263/4). In the case of the *Missale Parisiense* (Nos. 99, 100, and 101), of which I have examined three copies, the two copies in the Bibliothèque Ste-Geneviève have staves printed in the Canon only (these two copies differ in that one is printed on vellum and is richly illuminated), while the copy in the Morgan Library has space left for staves on one leaf before, and on the leaves after the Canon; here the staves and the music have been added later by hand.

2. The setting of the music may be different in different copies, and different founts may be used. This is the case with one *Missale Romanum*, printed by Sessa in Venice (Nos. 160 and 161). The copy in the Huntington Library is listed there as identical with the copy in the British Museum, both dated 'not after 1498'. Both copies have printed music, with seven staves to a page, but the form of the notes is different; and while in the Huntington copy music occurs before and in the Canon, the British Museum copy has printed music before the Canon only.

3. There may be a few differences in some musical notes. This is the case with the Gradual by Wenssler (No. 16), two copies of which are in the British Museum and one in the Huntington Library. On fol. 32a the initial ligature for the word *dicat* has the form •⦚ in the copy in the Huntington Library and in the copy IC 37134, and the form ⦚ in the copy IC 37132.

4. Finally, there are instances where it is obvious that mistakes have been corrected. Of the *Missale Sagiense* (No. 173) there are two versions.[2] In the earlier the page b8ᵛ has no space left for music; in the later the antiphon *Cum rex glorie*, following the benediction of the fire, and the *Exultet* of the benediction of the candles, were inserted, both text and music, the latter in manuscript.[3]

---

[1] Bibl. 40.   [2] Bibl. 33.

[3] We may mention here the deviation which occurs in the two editions of the *Missale Ratisponense* (nos. 110 and 111), printed seven years apart, one by Sensenschmidt and the other by Petzensteiner and Pfeyl. Here we find almost identical settings of the music, while parts of the text, the initials, and the rubrics, are different. In No. 110 on fol. 6b of the part with music, at the bottom of the

The cases mentioned under (2), (3), and (4), concern technical and bibliographical problems; this is not so with the books mentioned under (1). It will be noticed that the books listed there either have staves printed or space left for the music. In this respect copies of 'one' edition often vary. Sometimes books seem to have been published in two forms with a definite purpose, once as an ordinary edition and once as an *édition de luxe*, on vellum and with illuminated illustrations. The two editions of the *Missale Parisiense* in the Bibliothèque Ste-Geneviève (Nos. 99, 100) are a case in point. This distinction probably accounts also for the fact that in some books we have printed music and in others no music at all. As paper, and even more vellum, was a valuable material in the fifteenth century, the publisher was always ready to save space and paper by omitting the melodies. Moreover, by not printing the music, the expenses of special music type and labour to set it were saved. Such economic considerations may very well have influenced the printer in his choice of printing the melodies, or leaving space for them, or printing the text only.

Thus, in the course of some eight years, Wenssler printed five different editions or versions of the *Missale Basiliense*.[1] These have music printed as follows:

1.	*c.* 1480	Weale 153	Stillwell M 556	before and after the Canon		9 staves
2.	*c.* 1480	,, 153a	Augsburg City Lib.	only before ,, ,,		9 ,,
3.	ante 1485	,, 155	Cambridge U.L.	before and in ,, ,,	8 and 10	,,
4.	1486	? ?	Frankfurt-am-Main	?		10 ,,
5.	1488	,, 158	British Museum	before and in ,, ,,	10 and 7	,,

The first two of these editions are similar, as are the last three; but why Wenssler published five different editions in the course of eight years, and why he printed staves only in the edition of 1488, the year in which he printed his *Graduale* and his *Antiphonarium* with notes, I am not able to answer. As a possible explanation it might be suggested that he needed his musical founts for the *Graduale* and the *Antiphonarium*, and that the special craftsmen were so busy printing these books that they had no time to work on the Missal. As to the differences in the editions, perhaps the quantity of paper at his disposal made him print staves in two parts of one edition, and in one part only in some others. An edition of 1494 (Weale 159, now in the Bibliothèque Nationale) has no music at all.

A variation that occurs frequently is that in some copies of an edition the staves are printed, and in others we find merely spaces. This would confirm our assumption that the printing of the staves offered difficulties, quite apart from the problem of fitting notes and staves together. The two editions of the page, a word with stave and notes has been printed in the margin. The space had apparently not been estimated correctly. The mistake was corrected in the edition of 1492 (No. 111), where the printer found space for everything on the page by squeezing the notes together. This method of correcting and replacing single leaves of a piece of music is still in use today, as it was also in the period when music engraving was usual. Bibl. 28.

[1] The differentiation of the Basle Missals presents a problem. Weale lists ten editions, two of which do not figure in this catalogue (Weale 152 and 157). Of the others, one (Weale 154) was printed by Richel, and five by Wenssler; two (Weale 156 and 159a, copy in the Huntington Library) seem to come from other firms. Bibl. 40 and 44.

Pontificale (Nos. 229, 230) are interesting in this connexion. Both were printed in the same house, by Planck at Rome, in 1485 and 1497, and though the order of the text and the music is not identical, the earlier edition obviously served as a model for the later one. The technique employed in printing the staves is different: in the earlier edition we have a typical example of the use of metal rules, in the later of a single type filling the width of one column. Of the two techniques, the second is clearly neater and more even. In this case we can speak of an improvement in method from an earlier to a later edition. This cannot, however, be laid down as a general rule.

It has been pointed out several times that we cannot speak of a progressive development from editions without music to editions with music. It was not only technical ability which decided for the printer whether he would add the notes or print the staves only, or whether or not he would add the melodies to the text. Economic considerations played a large part in determining whether or not he would publish a more expensive edition, where he would use more paper, special musical type, and the threefold procedure necessary for printing text and melodies.

There is yet another factor which may have induced the printer to omit the music. The melodies of the Gregorian chant were not so uniform then as they are today. The Church Councils in Constance (1414–18) and Basle (1431–43) had long discussions concerning the reform and the standardization of liturgical music.[1] In different dioceses the form of the melodies might differ, and it was possible that the versions of the melodies which were common in one place were less known to a printer in another place. Thus, if a printer published a book with melodies not familiar to him, many mistakes could occur. We know of several editions that were prohibited or even destroyed because they contained too many mistakes. The *Missale Toletanum* (Weale 1529) was destroyed;[2] the two editions of the early Constance Breviary—this with no music—were prohibited; and Wenssler published an Utrecht service book that had to be destroyed.[3] We learn from the colophon in the Utrecht Missal, printed later in Paris, that Hopyl helped, for patriotic reasons, to establish a pure and reliable version of text and melodies.

To be on the safe side the printer would, in doubtful cases, leave the staves free, so that the notes could be added later by hand by someone who knew the local versions of the tunes. In only one case would I suggest that the notes were added later by actual printing: in the *Missale Sarum* ascribed generally to the Wenssler press. The setting of the text and the paper are his, but not the music. In 1487, shortly before he printed this Missal, he had suffered the misfortune of having been forced to destroy his edition of the Missal for Utrecht and must as a result have lost a considerable sum. With the Sarum Missal he would probably be more cautious, and therefore left space only, or possibly printed the staves.

---

[1] Incidentally, the importance of these discussions may have had something to do with the great number of service books for Basle and Constance.

[2] Bibl. 24.

[3] Bibl. 47.

That a printer other than Wenssler printed the music is obvious, because in the Sarum Missal the notes are roman, while in all his other liturgical books, Wenssler uses his typical gothic form.

It is not at all likely that the music was printed in England, as the only known English book, with music printed throughout, was published in 1500.[1] I would place the completion of the Missal at Rouen, where several service books for use in England were printed.[2] Apart from the Utrecht Missal printed by Higman and Hopyl, this is the only instance where I presume that the printing was done in two different shops.

The differences in the music in the liturgies for the monastic orders were still greater; it is probable, therefore, that most of the service books for these liturgies had no printed music, the books for the Dominicans being an exception.

Still another reason for not printing the music may be mentioned. Some of the liturgical books consist largely of extracts from the Bible, the Breviary, or the Diurnale. In these cases the separate issue has no music, because the book from which it was taken was printed without music. This probably accounts for the fact that so many psalters omit the music, apart from the fact that many of them were intended for private devotion and private prayer.

6. HISTORY

There is not much development in the history of the early printing of music. The printing of music started later than ordinary printing, around 1470, but once started it spread quickly. The earliest dated liturgical book with printed music is the *Missale Romanum*, printed in Rome by Ulrich Han in 1476; but Rome never developed anything like a school or centre for editions of liturgical music.

A. *Switzerland and Germany*

The *Graduale* set in the type of the printer of the Constance service books was published, I believe, at about the same time as the Missal printed by Han. This Gradual is one of the few books printed with black staves. Molitor, who had seen only fragments of the book, showed that it was printed from type.[3] It displays the gothic style in a form which I have not found in any other book; the forms for the single note and for the F-clef in particular are very individual. It uses ⁊ for a short ligature which is similar in style to the musical sorts cut for Wenssler.

While the Han Missal is the only achievement in our field at Rome for quite a time, Constance, Basle, and Strasbourg, all cities located within fairly easy reach of each other, seem to have formed a kind of region for the printing of liturgical incunabula with music.[4] There are ten editions with printed music from these cities for the years between 1476(?) and 1488, all printed in gothic type. Among these types that used by Wenssler is by far the most beautiful. Even if

---

[1] De Worde printed one small illustration on fol. 101 of Higden's *Polycronicon*, 1495.
[2] Bibl. 22.   [3] Bibl. 38.   [4] Bibl. 26.

the famous colophon[1] is not right in claiming that Wenssler and Kilchen invented the printing of music, it is certainly true that their type has outstanding aesthetic value. Wenssler's types were imitated or used later in Strasbourg at the press of Grüninger; and they turn up farther down the Rhine at Mainz in a Psalter by Schoeffer, printed in 1490, and in an unassigned Psalter printed in 1500.

Most books from German presses are printed in gothic type. We have items from Eichstädt, Würzburg, Bamberg, Augsburg, and Passau. Michael Reyser in Eichstädt produced a Psalter without music in 1485, and an *Obsequiale* with music in 1488. From the Würzburg Reyser we have two Psalters. The earlier is given by Bohatta[2] as two separate editions (Nos. 845/6), and dated *c.* 1475 and 1474/8. It is perhaps one edition only; the copy in the British Museum catalogue is described as 'not dated'. This Psalter, which is a liturgical book, not a separate edition of some Reyser Breviary, as suggested in the note to Nos. 5359 and 5356 of the *Gesamtkatalog*, has printed staves. Reyser's *Missale Herbipolense*, 1480, is not in the collections which I have described. Reyser did not use many ligatures, and his rows of single notes make a somewhat stiff impression. The earliest edition of Reyser mentioned in this catalogue is the *Missale* of 1481. This Missal and the *Missale Basiliense* printed by Richel (Weale 154) are considered to be the earliest missals with printed music in the German-speaking countries. Books with music printed by Reyser came out in 1481, 1482, 1484, 1491, and, the latest date so far noted, 1493. A Psalter, dated 1485 by Stillwell, has no music.

Reyser's publications were not so exclusively liturgical as Sensenschmidt's in Bamberg or as Ratdolt's in Augsburg. Ratdolt's output gives the impression of a modern liturgical publishing house, such as Pustet at Regensburg. His liturgical books have been described by Schottenloher,[3] who lists sixteen; to these we can add two more. Most of them have printed music:

1486	Missale for Gran, Venice	not in our list	no music
1487	Obsequiale, Augsburg	No. 222	music★
1489	Obsequiale, Augsburg	No. 223	music
1491	Missale Augustense	not in our list	music★
1491	Vigiliae	No. 255	music
1492	Missale Frisingense	No. 70	music★
1493	Obsequiale Frisingense	p. 35	no music
1493	Missale Brixiense	No. 50	music★
1493	Vigiliae Patavienses	not in our list	music
1494	Missale Pataviense	No. 106	music
1494	Graduale	No. 17	music
1494	Missale Aquilense	No. 38	music★
c. 1495	Obsequiale Brixiense	No. 14	music
1495	Antiphonarium	No. 9	music★
1496	Missale Augustense	No. 40	music★
1497	Obsequiale Saltzburgense	not in our list	?
1497	Missale Churiense	not in our list	?★

[1] Bibl. 36.   [2] Bibl. 3.   [3] Bibl. 45.

| 1498 Missale Pataviense | not in our list | ?* |
| 1499 Obsequiale Augustense | No. 224 | music |

(The * indicates that a facsimile from this book is in Schottenloher, Molitor, or Riemann.)[1]

The earliest book with music by Ratdolt is the *Obsequiale* of 1487. This is printed from woodblocks. Only in the edition of 1489 did Ratdolt print from type, and from then on most of his books containing music have the music printed from type. His output almost reaches in quantity the output of a modern industrialized age. His editions have always had a reputation for reliability, which they deserve. His style, however, strikes one as rather crude and commercialized.

In quantity, the output of the printers in Bamberg equals that of Ratdolt. In style they are less uniform. Sensenschmidt, besides producing on his own, worked also in collaboration with Petzensteiner and with Pfeyl. We also have books from each of these printers alone. Sensenschmidt's style is somewhat related to that of Georg Reyser. The books published by Pfeyl working alone are the only ones that show a more highly decorative style; we have three editions printed by him from 1499 to 1500.

Books with music printed in gothic style were also produced at Speyer, Nuremberg, Leipzig, and Passau. The style of Drach in Speyer is similar to that current in Bamberg, as is evident from the use of two clefs, one beneath the other, and one of them in the form of a catchnote. Stuchs was the foremost music printer in Nuremberg; he printed one book in association with Ryman. One book, signed by the Fratres Eremiti, is printed with the same type as that used by Stuchs. Kachelofen in Leipzig must have been familiar with the work of Stuchs, for both used the same C-clef. Petri's books, printed in Passau, show a clear and excellent technique; one of his books is the only edition so far known of an 'Historia'.

The only German printer to use the roman style was Arndes in Lübeck; his ligatures, especially, show highly individual and highly complicated forms.

B. *France*

The most interesting result of the present survey is the importance of the French contribution. Hitherto almost unknown, it equals the German, and is second only to the Italian production. Paris, with nineteen books with printed music during the incunabula period, cedes the first place as a city only to Venice which, of course, with its thirty-six books is by far in the lead.

The three French centres for the printing of liturgical books with music were Paris, Lyons, and Rouen, each having a special importance of its own. In Paris, besides the great industrialist Higman, from whose press came half the books mentioned, there were several printers who published one or two books with music. The earliest known French book with musical notes is a Missal by Jean Dupré, of 1489.[2] Dupré, who printed in Paris and in Chartres, published

[1] Bibl. 38, 43, 45.
[2] The problem whether there are two printers with the same name of Jean Dupré, or only one, has not been solved; Bibl. 11.

many service books, fifteen of which are included in our list; but only one of these has music. Gering and Rembolt collaborated in three very fine books. Gering, one of the earliest printers at Paris, working for the press of the Sorbonne, came from Constance in 1470. It is possible that, while there as a youth, he came into contact with the mysterious printer of the Constance service books and of the Gradual (No. 15). Alexander, as he signs his books, is Alexander Halial or Halyal; according to Renouard, he is Italian, though his name does not seem to indicate it.[1] Marnial or Maynyal is perhaps English; he printed later for Caxton.[2] Morand, Morin, Le Blanc, and Hodian are probably French. Their books were published in the fourteen-nineties, when the greater part of the profession was comprised of printers born in France.

The printing of music in the Paris editions is clear, and rather sober; the technique is careful and exact; the fitting of the music into the staves is excellent. The books of only one Paris printer, Michel de Toulouze, are unsatisfactory in this respect. In one of his books with secular music where he uses a notation resembling the plainchant notation, the fitting together is so inexact that it is often hard to recognize whether the notes and the clefs are supposed to be located on the lines or in the intervals.[3] His only liturgical book, a *Processionarium*, which contains music, is not available for study, its present owner being unknown.

The books printed at Lyons show Italian influence. The printers there use typical Italian forms. The only one who has a personal style, which differs also from the German forms, is Numeister. The Rouen printers resemble the Parisians in style. They are not as even and exact, but they are more individualistic. In this period Rouen forms an interesting link between France and England. It had belonged to England down to 1449, and the connexion remained strong throughout the fifteenth century.

It is interesting to note the places where the different issues of the Sarum Missal were published. Of the twelve editions listed by Weale,[4] ten figure in our list; of these three were printed at Rouen, one in 1492 and two in 1497; two were printed in Paris, two in Venice, one in Westminster, and one in London. Thus half the editions were published in France.[5] The printers of the two Missals published in England were French: Barbier and Notaire (Notary) of the Westminster edition, and Pynson of the London edition. Pynson was a native of Rouen, and was later naturalized as an English citizen.[6] From him comes the only known English incunable with all staves and notes completely printed—the Sarum Missal of 1500 (No. 186).

I should like at this point to refer again to the problem of the earliest Sarum Missal. The text and the staves of this book were printed by Wenssler at Basle; we know from documents[7] that he shipped service books to England; the music

---

[1] Bibl. 42.   [2] Bibl. 6.

[3] Toulouze must be credited with having been the first printer to use printing from type for measured music, both in a book of secular music and in a textbook. Bibl. 35.

[4] Some of the Missals listed by Weale seem to represent variants.

[5] Bibl. 22.   [6] Bibl. 18.   [7] Bibl. 36, 47.

was not printed by Wenssler, nor with his type; in some places in the book we can perceive that the music was printed after the staves; among the Wenssler service books with musical notes, it is the only one with roman forms and not with Wenssler's typical gothic form. I have not been able to identify the forms used, and as we know of no English liturgical incunable with music before 1500 it seems doubtful if the music was added by a printer in England. On the other hand, we know of several service books printed for English use at Rouen. It thus seems not unreasonable to suggest that the music in the Sarum Missal may have been added by some printer at Rouen.

The Sarum Manual printed at Rouen, a beautiful book with music by Olivier and Jean de Lorraine, belongs to the year 1501, and not to 1500 as listed by Bohatta (No. 740).

There are two other interesting books with music printed in France, Nos. 12 and 191. Probably both originated in Vienne in Dauphiné or some place near by. They are not listed in any local bibliography.[1]

C. *Italy*

Italy played the leading part in the production of liturgical books with printed music. Among the printers in smaller cities, Benedictus de Odis at Bologna has a highly individual style. His one liturgical book is referred to in the bibliographies as a Ritual. Neither the copy in the British Museum, however, nor that in the Huntington Library has a title or a colophon designating the book as a ritual, and the contents are identical with a *Liber Catechumeni*. The forms of the notes used by de Odis are rather crude and plump, though regular. The single note always has a stem, and the ligatures are formed by combining the single notes including the stems. This type has not been previously noticed elsewhere, nor is any other liturgical edition from this press known.

The type used by Britannicis in Brescia is similar to that of Hamman of Venice. Boninis, the other printer working at Brescia, introduced the Italian style to Lyons. To Rome belongs the distinction of being the first[2] to produce a book with music printed from type throughout, the *Missale Romanum* printed by Han in 1476. This work was printed with a roman type which has forms similar to those used previously in manuscripts, but which are at the same time similar to the forms used in modern service books. Han does not make use of many ligatures. The form of the C-clef, the only clef which he uses, is developed from the ligature for an ascending interval. Of later printers, Higman at Paris comes nearest to him, using type forms that are similar to his.

Han had one successor only at Rome, Stephan Planck, who published during the years 1485–97; his books reveal a high standard of fine and exact craftsmanship. His two editions of the *Pontificale* have already been mentioned (above, p. xxx) as evidence of one book being used as the model for a later one. As was

---

[1] Bibl. 8.

[2] The edition of the Commentary *super Magnificat* by Gerson, printed by Fyner in Esslingen in 1473, has a short example of some notes only, and no staves.

also mentioned, the two editions provide good examples of two different ways of setting the staves, with metal rules in the earlier, and with a single block in the later edition. When these two editions are compared side by side, the differences of the techniques come out very clearly. What material Planck has used for his single block is an unanswered question. I incline to the view that it was wood, as the colour is spread very evenly, and the block has not made a very sharp impression on the paper; still, we cannot exclude the possibility that the block was made of metal.

Of the Italian cities Venice, with an output of thirty-six books with printed music from fourteen presses, was by far the most productive. Incidentally, in the number of presses, Paris takes the second place, with seven presses and ten printers. Two Venetian printers of music stand out for the amount of their production; eleven books were published by Emericus of Spira, and eight by Hamman. The other printers in Venice: Arrivabene, Benaliis, Bevilacqua, Girardengus, Novimagio, Torresanus, Tortis, Scotus, and Sessa, each published one or two volumes with printed music. The Venetian style stands out by reason of its fluency and elegance. This is especially to be seen in the numerous editions in small quarto. A frequent use of ligatures is typical of the Venetian style, especially in the editions of Spira and Sessa. Venetian printers, probably because of the elegance of their printing, were responsible for many service books printed for foreign countries and cities.

Despite the pre-eminence of Rome and Venice, chronologically and quantitatively, Milan seems to have made the more interesting contributions to the development of printed music. The two Missals published in Milan in 1482 and in 1499, by Valdarfer and Pachel respectively, use neither roman nor gothic forms for the notes, but imitate the ductus of neumes. It is evident that Valdarfer's Missal served as a model for Pachel, and Pachel printed with the obsolete type after 1486, though he had already printed a book with the usual Roman type. What was the reason for this? It may be that, as both are Ambrosian Missals, which contain melodies differing from the ordinary roman versions, Pachel wished to express this difference by using an archaic form for the notes. Whether this was a characteristic of Ambrosian Missals can only be decided by an examination of other examples. Unfortunately the only other Ambrosian Missal which I have been able to examine has no music.

Pachel published one other book, in 1486, which is of interest in the history of music printing—the only edition of a *Hymnarium* with melodies. Both the copies mentioned in our catalogue are bound up with a Psalter by Pachel, which has no music, and a Magnificat, printed by Zarotus, in which space has been left for adding the melodies by hand.

D. *Spain*

From Spain we have five books with printed music. The earliest comes from Pegnitzer and his associates, 1491, two are from the press of Ungut and Polonus, 1494 and 1499, and two from Luschner, 1500. All use roman type with an inclination towards points and tails. The staves are wide, even in small books; the size of the notes is large and the form clear.

The contents of the Spanish liturgical books are interesting. Two of the five on our list are *Processionaria*. An investigation of these would be profitable for the scholar interested in the history of popular melodies. From Luschner we have the only example of a *Responsoriale* from the incunabula period. It gives the responses sung by the chorus during funeral services. It is usually listed in the catalogues as an *Antiphonale*, but Haebler recognized it as a *Responsoriale*.[1]

SUMMARY

Whether a liturgical book includes printed music, or whether it contains space for music, depends on the purpose for which the book was published. Books meant for private devotion and books written for use in schools did not have printed music. Titles, moreover, are not decisive and are often even misleading. Among the proper service books there are groups that collect only the parts of the liturgy which were read; these do not require the printing of melodies. If the music was not printed in books that require melodies, the reasons were probably economic. By so doing the printer could save space, paper, and labour. Further, it must be understood that in the incunabula period the music of the liturgy was not uniform, and the printer may well have omitted it in order to avoid making too many mistakes.

Technical reasons can scarcely have been the cause; otherwise a printer would not have published editions without music after he had printed editions with music, a practice that was not infrequent.

We have added to the list of liturgical books with music two types that have hitherto not been included in the bibliographies: the *Historia* and the *Responsoriale*. The *Historia* (or legend) was not classified as a liturgical book because most of the Histories are told in prose and meant to be read. There remain some groups of liturgical books, for which no copies with music have been found so far. It will not be surprising, however, if some day books from these groups turn up with music, the *Officia* in particular.

What is needed is a survey and a detailed description of the books that were used in the liturgy of the period. Only then, and when the bibliographies of liturgical books have been completed, and cleared of the items that do not belong to the liturgy—e.g. the *Manuale parochialium sacerdotum*—are we likely to know how many books would have to be surveyed, if we wanted to be complete.

With very few exceptions, the music in the service books is printed with movable type. Of the 150 or so books with music in our list, only two are undeniably printed from woodblocks. The textbooks, on the other hand, have their examples printed from woodblock, because this technique was economically appropriate for such printing. Here, too, the reason for the choice is not technical.

---

[1] Bibl. 24.

Introduction

Even if I do not feel quite as sure as Riemann,[1] who thought that 'alle wesent-lichen Probleme des Musikdrucks vor 1500 gelöst sind', I do think that the problems of the actual technique of printing music are nearing a solution. The main problem, however, is very different from what was previously supposed. It was the printing of the staves, not of the notes, that was the problem. The printer's difficulties were: the printing of the staves themselves, the distribution of the melodies to correspond to the text, and the fitting together of music and staves.

As regards the publication of liturgical books with music, there were editors or 'printers' who specialized in the printing of books with music, such as Higman at Paris, Ratdolt at Augsburg, and Spira at Venice. There were also presses that printed mostly ordinary books, but in addition printed some liturgical books with music.

Several firms published, at the same time, books with musical notes and books with staves only. It is thus apparent that the problem of cutting the types for notes had been solved, and that the difficulties lay in adding them.

Music may occur throughout a book, or it may be a separate part. In the latter case the text type is the same as in the rest of the text, except where a part has been inserted from another book, as in the case of the *Psalterium* and the *Hymnarium* by Pachel (No. 22) with the inserted *Magnificat* by Zarotus. Even if the text type is the same throughout, we cannot assume that the music was printed in the same press as the body of the text. It is possible that a foreign printer who had learnt how to print music was called in to help.

The *Missale Sarum* (No. 177) remains an unsolved problem. The text of this work was printed by Wenssler; the music, however, was not printed by him. A detailed comparison of musical types might bring us nearer a solution, but, so far, no types similar to those used in this Missal have been found. The other problematic item is the *Graduale* printed in the type of the Constance service books, but on paper which was otherwise used at Augsburg. When was this *Graduale* printed, and where, and who cut the types for the notes? Here again no similar types of notes have been noted.

Of the 450 books listed in our catalogue, 257 involve the printing of music, with staves only, or with staves and notes. Almost one-third of the books—a surprising number—have actual notes. It is also surprising that practically one-quarter of these were printed in France, a country from which no incunabula with printed music were previously known. Paris comes second in the number of books issued and in the number of printers at work in one town. I have been able to demonstrate the existence of one liturgical book with printed music from England. Half of the books with music were printed in Italy, approximately one-quarter in Germany, and one-quarter in France.

When I started this study, I did not know how far it would lead me. I had hoped to establish a means for ascertaining the printer of a book by the detailed description of the staves and the notes. This hope, however, has not been com-

[1] Bibl. 43.

pletely realized. The more detailed the description, the greater the number of variants. This is a difficulty which will not be solved until all copies of each edition of each work can be compared. If the splitting up of editions adds to our problems it is an advantage that by the method here established variants can be noted and made known.

This list must therefore be looked upon as an interim one. It can only become complete and final when all the material has been examined, exact copies and measurements of the musical forms and of the staves made, and a repertory of the forms of the notes completed.

BIBLIOGRAPHY

1. ADAM, J. L. 'Le Manuel de Coutances', *Revue catholique de Normandie*, vol. 18/19, 1909–10.
2. AUDIN, M. 'Les origines de la typographie musicale', *Le Bibliophile*, 1931–32.
3. BOHATTA, H. *Liturgische Bibliographie des XV. Jahrhunderts*, Wien, 1911.
4. BOHATTA, H. *Bibliographie der Livres d'heures*, Wien, 1924.
5. BRITISH MUSEUM. *Catalogue of books printed in the XVth century*, Introduction to vol. vi by V. Scholderer.
6. BÜHLER, C. 'George Maynyal', *The Library*, 4th Ser., XVIII, 1938.
7. *Bulletin de la Librairie Morgand*, N.S., 9 Nov. 1909, No. 504.
8. CHEVALIER, U. 'Manuscrits et incunables liturgiques du Dauphiné', *Société d'Archéologie de la Drôme, Bulletin*, 1920.
9. CHEVALIER, U. *Repertorium hymnologicum*, Bruxelles, 1920–1.
10. CLAUDIN, A. *Documents sur la typographie et la gravure en France aux XVe et XVIe siècles*, London, 1926.
11. CLAUDIN, A. *Histoire de l'imprimerie en France au XVe et au XVIe siècle*, Paris, 1900–14.
12. COLLIJN, I. *Katalog der Inkunabeln der Kgl. Bibliothek in Stockholm*, Uppsala, 1914–16.
13. COLLIJN, I. 'Lübecker Frühdrucke', *Zeitschrift des Vereins für Lübeckische Geschichte*, 9, 1908.
14. COLLIJN, I. *Manuale Upsalense, Stockholm 1487*, Stockholm, 1918.
15. COLLIJN, I. 'Ett nyfunnet blad av Canon missae 1458', *Nordisk tidskrift för bok- och biblioteksväsen*, XXI, 1934; and *Gutenberg-Jahrbuch*, 1935.
16. DALBANNE, C. *Typographie lyonnaise au XVe siècle*, Lyon, 1934.
17. DUFF, E. G. *Brief Notes on Twelve Liturgical Volumes of the XVth and XVIth Centuries*, London, 1910.
18. DUFF, E. G. *Early Printed Books*, London, 1893.
19. FALK, F. 'Die Agenden von Mainz', *Zeitschrift für Bibliothekswissenschaft*, 5, 1888.
20. FALKENSTEIN, C. K. *Geschichte der Buchdruckerkunst*, Leipzig, 1856.
21. FAVA, M. e GIOV. BRESCIANO. *La stampa a Napoli nel XV secolo*, Berlin, 1911–13.
22. FRÈRE, E. B. *Des livres de liturgie des églises d'Angleterre imprimés à Rouen dans les XVe et XVIe siècles*, Rouen, 1867.
23. *Gesamtkatalog der Wiegendrucke.*
24. HAEBLER, K. *Bibliografía ibérica del siglo XV*, La Haya; Leipzig, 1903, 1917.
25. HAEBLER, K. 'Joh. Grüninger, der Drucker des Missale mit dem Kanon Peter Schoeffers', *Beiträge zur Inkunabelkunde*, N.F., IV, 1911.
26. HARRISSE, H. *Les Premiers Incunables bâlois 1471–1484*, Paris, 1902.
27. HIND, A. M. *History of Engraving and Etching*, London, 1927.
28. HIRSCH, P. 'A Discrepancy in Beethoven', *Music and Letters*, XIX, 1938.
29. KELCHNER, E. *Der Pergamentdruck der Agenda Ecclesiae Moguntinensis von 1480*, Frankfurt, 1885.
30. KINKELDEY, O. 'Music and Music Printing in Incunabula', *Papers of the Bibliographical Society of America*, 1932.
31. KLEMMING, G. *Sveriges äldre liturgiska literatur*, Stockholm, 1879.
32. LENHART, J. M. 'Pre-reformation Printed Books', *Franciscan Studies*, 14, 1935.
33. LE VERDIER, P. *L'Atelier de Guillaume Le Talleur*, Rouen, 1916.
34. MEYER, K. 'The Liturgical Music Incunabula in the British Museum', *The Library*, 4th Ser., XX, 1940.

35. MEYER, K. 'Michel de Toulouze', *Music Review*, 1946.

36. MEYER, K. 'Musikdruck in den liturgischen Inkunabeln von Wenssler und Kilchen', *Gutenberg-Jahrbuch*, 1935.

37. MEYER, K. 'Music-printing 1473–1934', *Dolphin*, 2, 1935.

38. MOLITOR, R. *Deutsche Choral-Wiegendrucke*, Regensburg, 1904.

39. NIJHOFF, W. *L'Art typographique dans les Pays-Bas pendant les années 1500 à 1540*, La Haye, 1902–35.

40. PFISTER, A. 'Vom frühsten Musikdruck in der Schweiz', *Festschrift Gustav Binz zum 70. Geburtstag*, Basle, 1935.

41. POLAIN, M. L. *Catalogue des livres imprimés au quinzième siècle des bibliothèques de Belgique*, Bruxelles, 1932.

42. RENOUARD, PH. 'Imprimeurs parisiens', *Revue des bibliothèques*, 32/44, 1898, 1922–34.

43. RIEMANN, H. 'Notenschrift und Notendruck'. *Festschrift . . . C. G. Roeder*, 1896.

44. SCHOLDERER, V. 'Michael Wenssler and his Press at Basel', *The Library*, 3rd Ser., VI, 1912.

45. SCHOTTENLOHER, K. *Die liturgischen Druckwerke Erhard Ratdolts*, Mainz, 1922.

46. STEELE, R. 'What 15th Century Books are about?', *The Library*, N.S., IV, V, VI, VIII, 1903–7.

47. STEHLIN, K. 'Regesten', *Archiv für Geschichte des Buchhandels*, 11/14, 1888/91; 20, 1897.

48. TARDIEU, A. *Histoire généalogique de Clermont-Ferrand*, 1871.

49. *Veröffentlichungen der Gesellschaft für Typenkunde*, nos. 1323/4.

50. VOULLIÉME, E. *Der Buchdruck Kölns*, Köln, 1903.

51. WEALE, W. H. J. *Bibliographia liturgica. Catalogus Missalium*, ed. H. Bohatta, London, 1928.

52. WEALE, W. H. J. *Historical Music Loan Exhibition . . . 1885. A descriptive catalogue*, London, 1886.

53. WOLF, JOH. *Handbuch der Notationskunde*, Leipzig, 1913–19.

54. WOLF, JOH. 'Verzeichnis der musiktheoretischen Inkunabeln', *Veröffentlichungen der Musik-Bibliothek Paul Hirsch*, I, 1922.

ABBREVIATIONS

BMC	British Museum. *Catalogue of Books printed in the XVth century.*
Br.M.	British Museum.
Boh.	H. Bohatta. *Liturgische Bibliographie des XV. Jahrhunderts,* 1911.
Cambridge U.L.	University Library, Cambridge.
Cat. Maz.	P. Marais. *Catalogue des incunables de la Bibliothèque Mazarine,* 1893, and Supplement by W. A. Copinger, 1893.
Cat. S.G.	C. F. Daunou. *Catalogue des incunables de la Bibliothèque Ste-Geneviève,* 1892. The new catalogue by L. M. Michon: *Inventaire des incunables de la Bibliothèque Ste-Geneviève,* 1943, yielded information on one more book, the missal Weale 843; the missal Weale 124 is not listed in either of the two catalogues.
GK	*Gesamtkatalog der Wiegendrucke.*
Haebler	K. Haebler. *Bibliografía ibérica del siglo XV,* 1904, 1917.
Hain	L. Hain. *Repertorium bibliographicum,* 1862–38.
Harvard	Harvard University Library.
Huntington	Huntington Library, Pasadena, California.
Lib.	K. Meyer. 'Liturgical Music Incunabula in the British Museum', in *The Library,* 4th Ser., xx, 1940.
Oates	J. C. T. Oates. *A Catalogue of the Fifteenth-century Printed Books in the University Library, Cambridge,* 1954.
Oxf. Bodl.	Bodleian Library, Oxford.
Paris Ars.	Bibliothèque de l'Arsenal, Paris.
Paris BN.	Bibliothèque Nationale, Paris.
Paris Maz.	Bibliothèque Mazarine, Paris.
Paris S.G.	Bibliothèque Ste-Geneviève, Paris.
Pellechet	M. Pellechet. *Catalogue général des incunables des bibliothèques publiques de France,* 1897–1905.
Proctor	R. Proctor. *An Index to the Early Printed Books in the British Museum,* 1898.
Stillwell	M. B. Stillwell. *Incunabula in American Libraries,* 1940.
Voulliéme	E. Voulliéme. *Der Buchdruck Kölns,* 1903.
Weale	W. H. J. Weale. *Bibliographia liturgica,* 1928.

NOTE

Each entry includes the name of the book, the place of printing, the printer, and the year, as far as these are known. No indication is given whether this information is obtained from the book or from bibliographies.

Weale and Bohatta numbers are given; supplemented on occasion by references to special bibliographies.

Shelf numbers are added for items in the British Museum, the Bodleian, and the Paris libraries. The code letters and numbers are explained on p. xvi of the Introduction.

Books referred to in the section D:—4 of the descriptions are listed with full title in the Bibliography.

All books which have any kind of connexion with printing music are numbered. Those without music have been included to indicate that they have been seen and studied, but they are not numbered.

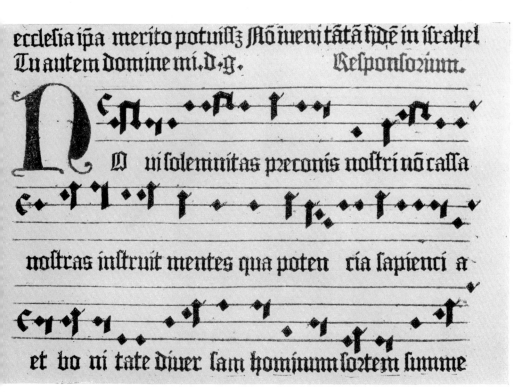

ecclesia ipa merito potuiss̄ Nō iueni tātā fidē in ifrahel
Tu autem domine mi.d.g. Responforium.

O ui folemnitas preconis noftri nō caffa

noftras inftruit mentes qua poten cia fapienci a

et bo ni tate diuer fam hominum fortem fumme

1. Notes in gothic style. The only known *Historia* printed with music. Cat. no. 21

Iuine pacis et indulgētie

munere fupplicantes.ex toto

corde.et ex tota mente.

Precamur tc.

DO mi ne miferere.

2. Notes imitating neumes. *Missale Ambrosianum,*
1482. Cat. no. 35

3. Notes in roman style. *Missale Romanum*, 1476. Cat. no. 119

4. Staves set with several type pieces. *Missale Pictaviense*, 1498. Cat. no. 107

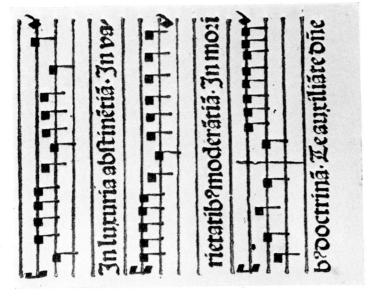

6. Staves with one type for the width of the line. *Pontificale*, 1497. Cat. no. 230

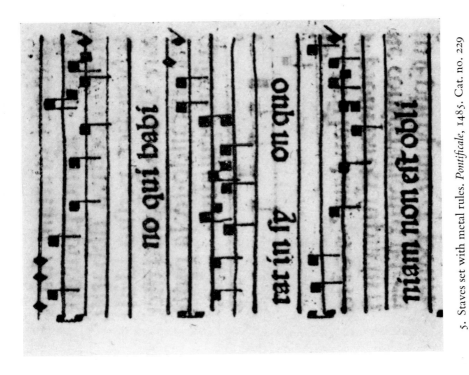

5. Staves set with metal rules. *Pontificale*, 1485. Cat. no. 229

7. Probably the earliest book with music printed from type. *Graduale Constantiense*. Cat. no. 15

8. Book printed by two different presses. *Missale Sarum,* c. 1489. Cat. no. 177

9. The only known *Hymnarium* with printed music. Milan, 1487. Cat. no. 22

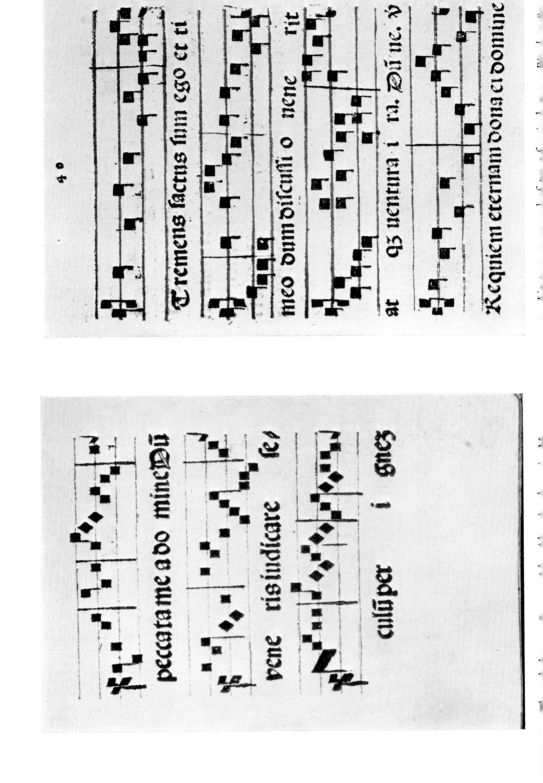

12. The only known English incunable with printed music.
Missale Sarum, 1500. Cat. no. 186

1. AGENDA ARGENTINENSIS
Basle: Wenssler and Kilchen, 1488
Paris Maz. 1139
GK. 460; Boh. 3
not in Pellechet
A:— 1; 6: throughout.
B:— 2; 3: ⌂ ⌂ ⌂ ⌂ ⌂ for different intervals; 5: ⌁ not completely identical; 6: stems at the beginning of a word.
C:— 1: 1; 2: 5; 3: 4; 4: red; 6: a, d(2); 7: b(c?).
D:— 1: C and F ⌂⌂; in the border ♭ ; 2: ⌁ 3: no; 4: two sets of initials; Lit.: Weale, *Historical Music Loan Exhibition*, p. 67; in GK. Furter? post 1500?

AGENDA, SIVE EXEQUIALE, ARGEN-
TINENSIS
Strasbourg: Pruess, *c.* 1500
Paris BN. Rés. B. 27819
GK. 459a; Boh. 4
Pellechet 233
A:— 5.
D:— 4: 8°; Pellechet states 'Basileae, Wenssler *ou* Argentine: Pruess', apparently mixing up this and the preceding item, which latter is not listed in Pellechet; the above item is possibly identical not only with GK. 459a, but with GK. 455 and 456. GK. 457 has music; all editions with the Creed in German.

2. AGENDA BAMBERGENSIS
Bamberg: Petzensteiner, Sensenschmidt and Pfeyl, 1491.
Br.M. IA. 2652
GK. 461; Boh. 5; Lib. 1
A:— 1; 6: throughout.
B:— 2; 3: ⌂ ⌂ for different intervals; 4: in part.
C:— 1: 1; 2: 5; 3: 4; 4: red; 6: a, d(2); 7b.
D:— 1: C and F ⌂ ⌂ one beneath the other in the border; 2: none; 3: bars separating words occasionally.

AGENDA
See also Benedictionale, Exequiale.

AGENDA BREVIS ET PERUTILIS
Venice: Hamman pro Volkarth, 1495
Stillwell A 148
GK. 453; Boh. 17 (2?)
A:— 5.
D:— 4: small 8°; printer's sign at the end; 'Ordo baptizandi' in MS. bound in at the beginning. Lit.: Duff, *Brief notes on Twelve liturgical volumes of the 15th and 16th centuries*; Hain as well as Bohatta, nos. 2 and 17, have mixed up the several Agendas printed by Hamman.

3. AGENDA HERBIPOLENSIS
Würzburg: Reyser, 1482
Br.M. IB. 10507
Paris BN. Rés. B. 499
Stillwell A 151
GK. 463; Boh. 7; Lib. 2
A:— 1; 6: throughout.
B:— 2; 3: ⌂ ⌂ ⌂; 5: straight, no points; 6: no stems.
C:— 1: 1; 2: 7; 3: 4; 4: red; 5; 7b(?).
D:— 1: C and F ⌂, ⌂ or ⌂, ♭ ; 2: ⌁ ; 3: bars separating words and occasionally sentences; 4: Colophon and engraving with coat of arms at the end of preface. The staves, generally running over the whole page, are twice shortened by the same length in front to make space for the initials which are partly MS.

AGENDA LUBICENSIS
Br.M. IA. 9983; GK. 465
See Benedictionale.

4. AGENDA MAGDEBURGENSIS
Magdeburg: Moritz Brandis, 1497
Paris BN. Rés. B. 2944
GK. 467; Boh. 10; Pellechet 235
A:— 2; 6: throughout.
C:— 1: 1; 2: 6; 3: 4; 4: red; 5; 7c.
D:— 4: Bohatta 'cum notis musicis(!)'.

AGENDA MOGUNTINENSIS
Mainz: Numeister, 1480
Stillwell A 152
GK. 468; Boh. 13

A:— 5.

D:— 4: the fragments of the book in the Library of Congress have been supplemented from the copy in the Rylands Collection at Manchester. Lit.: Kelchner, *Der Pergamentdruck der Agenda Ecclesiae Moguntinensis von 1480*; Falk, 'Die Agenden von Mainz'.

5. AGENDA MOGUNTINENSIS
   Strasbourg: Pruess, *c.* 1490
   Br.M. IB. 1734
   GW. 469; Boh. 12
A:— 1; 6: throughout.
B:— 2; 3: ♫ mostly 4; 6: with stems.
C:— 1: 1; 2: 9; 3: 3; 4: black; 5.
D:— 1: F 𝄢; 2: ♮; 3: none. 4: The clefs and guides printed with type, the notes and staves probably from wood-block; the facsimile in Molitor, pl. 16, from the copy in Mainz, Stadtbibliothek, has a fourth line in red added by hand.

6. AGENDA PATAVIENSIS
   Passau: Petri, 1490
   Stillwell A 153
   not in GK.; Boh. 16
A:— 1; 6: throughout.
B:— 2; 3: ♩ ♫ ♫ ♫; 5: small points, occasionally ♦ and ◊; 6: both forms: a stem to designate beginning or end of a word, ♩ and 𝅗𝅥.
C:— 1: 1; 2: 7; 3: 4; 4: red; 5; 7c(?).
D:— 1: C and F 𝄢𝄢; 2: ╱; 3: none; 4: Facs. Molitor, pl. 11.

7. AGENDA, SEU BENEDICTIONALE, PATAVIENSIS
   Venice: Hamman pro Petri, 1498
   Stillwell A 154
   GK. 473; Boh. 18
A:— 1; 6: throughout.
B:— 2; 3: ♩ ♩ ♫ for different intervals; 4: in some parts; 5: straight, no points; 6: no stems.
C:— 1: 1; 2: 6; 3: 4; 4: red; 5; 7a.
D:— 1: C and F 𝄢𝄢; 2: ◡ occasionally;

3: none; 4: black and red initials, Facs. Molitor, pl. 18.

AGENDA PRAGENSIS
   Pilsen: Printer of the Missale Pragense, *c.* 1480
   Stillwell A 155
   GK. 475; not in Boh.
A:— 5.
D:— 4: The book, without title, starts 'In vigilia epiphanie benedictio salis et aque'; initials and rubrics in MS.; the rubrics indicate several times 'chorus'; in the catalogue of the Library of Congress listed as Benedictionale; the GK. states one copy only, at Prague.

8. AGENDA PRO MORTUIS
   Bamberg: Sensenschmidt, *c.* 1487
   Stillwell A 149
   Cambridge UL., Oates 273
   GK. 479; not in Boh.
A:— 4; 6: fols. 12b-15a.
C:— 1: 1; 2: 7 and 8.
D:— 4: Incipit—Exhortatio beati Anselmi canthuariensis Episcopi ad fratrem moriturum; no colophon.

9. ANTIPHONARIUM
   Augsburg: Ratdolt, 1495
   Br.M. IB. 6753
   Oxf. Bodl. Inc. e. G. V. 1495/1
   Stillwell A 682
   GK. 2062; Boh. 23; Lib. 4
A:— 1; 6: throughout.
B:— 2; 3: ♩ ♫; 5: straight ◊ and ♭; 6: both forms.
C:— 1: 1; 2: 9; 3: 4; 4: red; 6: a, d(2); 7: a.
D:— 1: C, F, and G, one beneath the other 𝄢𝄢 and 𝄞, ♭ and ♮; 2: ╱; 3: bars occasionally only; 4: called 'Antiffanarium' in title and colophon; facs. Schottenloher, *Die liturgischen Druckwerke Erhard Ratdolts*, pls. 30, 31.

ANTIPHONARIUM
   Montserrat: Luschner, 1500
   See Responsoriale.

10. ANTIPHONARIUM ORD. S. HIERONYMI
   Seville: Compañeros Alemanes, *c.* 1491
   Paris BN. Rés. Vél. 807
   GK. 2066; Boh. 25

A:— 1; 6: throughout.

B:— 1; 3: ⟨symbols⟩; 4: sometimes broken up; 5: ♮; 6: no stems.

C:— 1: 1; 2: 7; 3: 4; 4: red; 5; 7c.

D:— 1: C and F ⟨symbols⟩; 2: ⟨symbol⟩; 3: bars between sentences.

11. ANTIPHONARIUM ROMANUM

Venice: Spira pro Giunta, *c.* 1499
Br.M. IC. 24247
GK. 2061; Boh. 27; Lib. 3

A:— 1; 6: throughout.

B:— 1; 3: ⟨symbols⟩ besides the normal ligatures, that is joining two notes rising or descending; 5: straight; 6: with stems.

C:— 1: 1; 2: 7; 3: 4; 4: red; 5; 7 a and b.

D:— 1: C and F ⟨symbols⟩, ♭ and ♮ for ♮; 2: ⟨symbol⟩; 3: double bars between words; 4: Elephant folio, 3 leaves introduction dealing with the Gregorian chant.

12. BAPTESIMALE VIENNENSE

s.l.; s.typ.; s.a.
Paris Ars. 8° T. 2366
Hain 13927?

A:— 2, and 3 towards the end only.

C:— 1: 1; 2: 5; 3: 4; 4: red; 5; 7a.

D:— 4: Baptesimale scdm usum viennen. dioces. Sanctus Mauricius; with the woodcut of the saint on the title; in the catalogue of the Arsenal called 'Manuale'; perhaps identical with Boh. 1057 and Hain 13927 Ritualis liber Ecclesiae Viennensis; not listed in the local bibliographies of Chevalier and Dalbanne.

BENEDICTIONALE, *see* Agenda, Ceremoniale, Obsequiale.

13. BENEDICTIONALE LUBICENSE

Lübeck: Matthäus Brandis, *c.* 1485
Br.M. IA. 9883
GK. 465; Boh. 8

A:— 4; 6: In 'benedictio cerei pascalis' and 'Kyrie eleyson'.

C:— 1: 1; 2: 9.

D:— 4: This book is called 'Agenda' in the Index of the *BMC.*, in Bohatta, and in GK.; GK. 465 gives the Br.M. shelf-number as IA. 9985, and calls the printer 'Printer of the Benedictionale'; Bohatta lists this book twice, as no. 8 Agenda, and no. 1051 Rituale.

BENEDICTIONALE PATAVIENSE, *see* Agenda.

14. CEREMONIALE BRIXINENSE

Augsburg: Ratdolt, *c.* 1495
Br.M. IB. 6791
Stillwell O 3
Boh. 745?; Lib. 6.

A:— 1; 6: throughout.

B:— 2; 3: ⟨symbols⟩, for the greater part 4; 5: straight; 6: no stems.

C:— 1: 1; 2: 6; 3: 4; 4: red; 5; 7a.

D:— 1: C and F ⟨symbols⟩ and ⟨symbol⟩; 2: ⟨symbol⟩ and ⟨symbol⟩; 3: bars between sentences; 4: the title reads 'Ceremoniale sive Obsequiale'; listed by Bohatta and Stillwell as Obsequiale; by Bohatta dated 1487; not in Schottenloher.

CEREMONIALE BURSFELDENSE
Marienthal: Fratres Communes, *c.* 1474
Br.M. IA. 9706 and 9712
Paris BN. Rés. H. 734 and B. 3327
Boh. 557?; Lib. 5; Pellechet 3137

A:— 5.

D:— 4: consists of a Ceremoniale and an Ordinarium; the copy of the Br.M. has been broken up into the Ceremoniale (IA. 9706) and the Ordinarium (IA. 9712); in the Paris copies the order is: Ordinarium, Ceremoniale.

CEREMONIALE BURSFELDENSE
Marienthal: Fratres Communes, post 1474
Paris BN. Rés. H. 2144

A:— 5.

D:— 4: this copy contains: 1. Martyrologium O.S.B., 2. Ceremonie, 3. Ordinarium; 1 leaf, 105 numb. ll.; 35 lines; this is a later edition of the previous item; not listed in Pellechet and Bohatta as different from preceding item; but listed as missal in Weale–Bohatta, no. 1679.

The Ceremoniale Romanum, Bohatta 559 and Pellechet 3138, is not a service book; it describes the laws of the Conclave; 'liber primus de loco conclavis primum deligendo'.

CEREMONIALE SARUM, *see* Ordinarium.

COLLECTARIUS MOGUNTINUS
s.loc.; s.typ.; s.a.
Oxf. Bodl. Auct. I. Q. V. 50
GK. 7160; Boh. 560/1

A:— 5.

D:— 4: Incipit Calendarium et enumeratio, explanatio; on leaf 10b 'Moguntina ecclesia' mentioned; after the calendar follows list of spoken prayers through the cursus, then the prayers for special ceremonies. Exhortatio beati ancelmi canthuariensis is the only service devoted to a saint, listed under collecta ordinaria in the index. On the back of the contemporary binding a later shield 'Augsburg—Ratdolt, 1490'.

Following Bohatta 560: s.l., s.typ., *c.* 1485; following Cop. II. 1681 and Bohatta 561: Bamberg, Sensenschmidt, *c.* 1480; following GK.: written for the Bursfeldian Benedictines, printed Bamberg, Sensenschmidt, 1485.

COMPENDIUM BENEDICTINUM,
see Directorium.

COMPENDIUM DIVINORUM OFFICIORUM
Paris: Dupré, 1496
Paris SG. OE. 15.824, cat. 819
A:— 5.
D:— 4: not listed in Bohatta; in GW. under Joh. Muneratus, that is Jean le Munerat, cochantre du Collège de Navarre; not listed under its author in the catalogue of printed books of the Bibliothèque Nationale.

COMPENDIUM ORD. FRATRUM PRAEDICATORUM
Venice: Frankfordia, 1483
Paris BN. Rés. B. 27767
GK. 8516; Boh. 564
A:— 5.
D:— 4: part of Diurnale.

COMPENDIUM ORD. S. VINCENTII
Mâcon: Wenssler, 1493
Paris BN. Rés. Vél. 1608
not in GK.; Boh. 563
A:— 5.
D:— 4: part of Diurnale.

COMPENDIUM ROMANUM
Venice: Torresanus and de Blavis, 1488
Cambridge UL., Oates 1861
not in Boh.
GK. 8501
A:— 5.

DIRECTORIUM AUGUSTENSE
Augsburg: Baemler, 1495
Stillwell D 218
GK. 8445; Boh. 572
A:— 5.
D:— 4: Title 'Breviarium pro Dyocesi ecclesie Augustensis'; colophon 'Breviarium secundum chorum Ecclesie Augustensis'; on last leaf 'littere dominicales'.

DIRECTORIUM AUGUSTENSE
Augsburg: Ratdolt, 1497
Br.M. IA. 6773
Paris BN. Rés. B. 27904
Stillwell D 219
GK. 8446; Boh. 573; Pellechet 4339; not in Schottenloher
A:— 5.

DIRECTORIUM BASILIENSE
Basle: Wenssler, 1480
Paris SG. OE. 15.750, cat. 322
GK. 8447; Boh. 574; Pellechet 4340
A:— 5.

DIRECTORIUM BENEDICTINUM
Montserrat: Luschner, 1500
Br.M. IA. 54321
Stillwell X 14
Haebler 235
A:— 5.
D:— 4: copy in Br.M. bound together with Exercitationes; both manc.; listed in GK. and Stillwell under Ximenes de Cisneros; title Directorium or Compendium.

DIRECTORIUM CONSTANTIENSE
Germany: Printer of the Constance Service books, not after 1476.
Br.M. IB. 38312
Paris BN. Rés. B. 576
Boh. 575; Lib. 7; Pellechet 4341
A:— 5.
D:— 4: beautiful initials similar to some used by Wenssler.

DIRECTORIUM CONSTANTIENSE
s.l.; s. typ.; *c.* 1496
Paris Maz. 899, cat., p. 484
GK. 8451; Boh. 576; Pellechet 4342
A:— 5.
D:— 4: in GK. dated 1501 and ascribed to Ratdolt; this ascription seems to go back to a MS. entry in the copy of the catalogue in

the Mazarine, where the edition seems to have been mixed up with the Directorium Augustense, Paris, BN. Rés. B. 27904.

DIRECTORIUM MOGUNTINUM
Mainz: Petrus de Friedberg, 1492
Br.M. IA. 363
Boh. 579; Lib. 8
A:— 5.

DIRECTORIUM MOGUNTINUM
Mainz: Petrus de Friedberg, *c.* 1494
Paris BN. Rés. B. 3047
Boh. 580
not in Pellechet
A:— 5.
D:— 4: manc., different from the preceding item.

DIRECTORIUM MOGUNTINUM
Cologne: Quentell, *c.* 1494
Cambridge UL., Oates 756
Boh. 581
not in Voulliéme
A:— 5.

DIRECTORIUM SALTZBURGENSE
Nuremberg: Stuchs, 1497
Br.M. IA. 8111
Oxf. Bodl. Inc. e. G. 6.1
Cambridge UL., Oates 1096
Stillwell D 220
Boh. 583 and 1055
A:— 5.
D:— 4: listed by Bohatta under Directorium and under Rituale.

DIRECTORIUM SARUM
Antwerp: Leeu, 1488
Br.M. IA. 49789
Oxf. Bodl. I. Q. V. 8
Cambridge UL., Oates 3912
Boh. 585
A:— 5.
D:— 4: Incipit prologus in tractatum . . . qui dicitur Directorium sacerdotum. Explicit ordinale secundum usum sarum. Printer's sign at the end.

DIRECTORIUM SARUM
Westminster: Caxton, 1489
Oxf. Bodl. S. Selden d. 11
Br.M. frg. 55016 (5); (55007)
Boh. 584?
A:— 5.

DIRECTORIUM SARUM
Westminster: de Worde, 1495
Cambridge UL., Oates 4123
Boh. 586
A:— 5.

DIRECTORIUM SARUM
Westminster: de Worde, s.a.
Cambridge UL., Oates 4147
not in Boh.
A:— 5.

DIRECTORIUM SARUM
London: Pynson, 1497
Br.M. IA. 55504
Boh. 587
A:— 5.

EXEQUIALE, *see* Agenda, Obsequiale.

15. GRADUALE
Augsburg?: Zainer? s.a.
Br.M. IB. 6883
Boh. 699; Lib. 12
A:— 1; 6: throughout.
B:— 2; 3: ⬩ ⬩; 5: curved, with points, in ligatures to start ⬩ and to end ⬩; 6: mostly with stems.
C:— 1: 1; 2: 7; 3: 5; 4: black, but with the F-line sometimes drawn over in red; 6: a, d(2); 7c.
D:— 1: C and F ⬩ ⬩; 2: ⬩; 4: Lit.: facs. in Molitor, pl. II from the fragment in Tübingen; types of the text identical with the Breviarium Constantiense, 'not after 1473', GK. 5315; Gesellschaft für Typenkunde 1323/24; facs. of Brev. in A. Rosenthal, cat. 11, 1941, no. 108; see Introduction, p. xxxi.

16. GRADUALE
Basle: Wenssler and Kilchen, 1488
Br.M. IC. 37132 and 37134, both manc.
Cambridge UL., Oates 2745
Paris BN. Rés. B. 624
Stillwell G 299
Boh. 701, 702; Lib. 9
A:— 1; 6: throughout.
B:— 2; 3: ⬩ ⬩; 5: slightly curved, with points; 6: both forms.
C:— 1: 1; 2: 8; 3: 4; 4: red; 6: a, d(2), and at the bottom 1 line; 7b.
D:— 1: C and F ⬩ ⬩; 2: ⬩; 4: two editions,

but almost identical, with only small differences, e.g. on fol. 32a the initial ligature
at 'dicat' has the form ⟨symbol⟩ in IC. 37132, and
the form ⟨symbol⟩ in IC. 37134 and in the copy
in the Huntington Lib.

17. GRADUALE
Augsburg: Ratdolt, 1494
Cambridge UL., Oates 965
Stillwell 300
Boh. 703
A:— 1; 6: throughout.
B:— 2; 3: ⟨symbols⟩; 5: straight, no points;
6: both forms.
C:— 1: 1; 2: 9; 3: 4; 4: red; 6: d(2); 7a.
D:— 1: C, F and G ⟨symbols⟩ and ♭; 2: ⟨symbol⟩;
3: no bars; 4: manc.

18. GRADUALE MOGUNTINUM
Speyer: Drach, 1500
Br.M. IB. 8668
Lib. 10
A:— 1; 6: throughout.
B:— 2; 3: ⟨symbols⟩, mostly 4: ⟨symbols⟩; 5:
straight, no points; 6: both forms.
C:— 1: 1; 2: 7; 3: 4; 4: red; 6: a, d(2); 7a.
D:— 1: C and F ⟨symbols⟩ and ♭; 2: ⟨symbol⟩; 3: bars
occasionally only; 4: the sections of type
used for the staves are so small that it
reminds one of modern music print from
type; printer's sign at end.

19. GRADUALE SUECICUM
Lübeck: Arndes, 1493
Oxf. Bodl. and Cambridge UL., 1 fol. each
in: Klemming, Sveriges äldre liturgiska
literatur; 1 fol. Br.M. Hirsch Cat. IV
Curiosa
Stillwell G 302
Boh. 705
A:— 1; 6: throughout.
B:— 1; 3: ⟨symbols⟩; 5: straight;
6: with stems.
C:— 1: 1; 2: 10; 3: 4; 4: red; 5; 7b(c).
D:— 1: C and F ⟨symbols⟩ and ♭ = ♮; 2: ⟨symbol⟩;
3: no bars; 4: description completed from
the copy in Stockholm (Collijn, *Katalog*,
p. 464); ascribed by Klemming and Bohatta
to Ghotan.

20. GRADUALE ROMANUM. Edited by
Franciscus de Brugis

Venice: Spira, 1499–1500
Br.M. IC. 24240
Stillwell G 301
Boh. 704; Lib. 11
Pellechet 5288
A:— 1; 6: throughout.
B:— 1; 3: ⟨symbols⟩ and the usual forms,
and that frequently; 5: straight; 6: with
stems.
C:— 1: 1; 2: 7; 3: 4; 4: red; 5; 7b, space for
initials has been left free.
D:— 1: C and F ⟨symbols⟩, ♮ = ♭; 2: ⟨symbol⟩; 3: single
and double bars between words.

21. HISTORIA DE SANCTO LEOPOLDO
Passau: Petri, s.a.
Br.M. IB. 11346
A:— 1; 6: throughout.
B:— 2; 3: ⟨symbols⟩; 4: for a great part; 5:
straight, small points ⟨symbols⟩; 6: generally no
stems.
C:— 1: 1; 2: 8; 3: 4; 4: red; 5; 7c.
D:— 1: C and F ⟨symbols⟩; 2: ⟨symbol⟩; 3: no bars.

HISTORIAE PLURIMORUM SANC-
TORUM, Louvain: Jo. de Paderborn,
1485, Cambridge (UL.) = Voragine,
Legenda Aurea.

Hymnarium—only the books with the titles
Hymnarium or Hymni are considered; the
Expositiones are excluded, if thus mentioned
in the title and in the bibliographies.

HYMNARIUM
Basle: Furter, 1497
Oxf. Bodl. Auct. I. Q. VII. 81
Boh. 685 = Boh. 1085
= Expositiones.

HYMNARIUM
Burgos: Federigo di Basilea, 1493.
Stillwell E 119
Haebler 251
= Expositiones; listed in GK. as Hymni.

HYMNARIUM
Cologne: Koelhof, the elder, 1480
Br.M. IA. 3504
Boh. 708; Voulliéme 603
A:— 5.
D:— 4: Voulliéme, *c.* 1477.

HYMNARIUM
Cologne: Quentell, 1492–1500
Voulliéme 604–°609
= Expositiones.

HYMNARIUM
Deventer: Pafraet, *c.* 1490
Br.M. IA. 47742
Boh. 710
A:— 5.

22. HYMNARIUM
Milan: Pachel and Scinzenzeler, 1486
Br.M. IB. 26533
Huntington Lib. Cat., inc. no. 101724
Boh. 946; Lib. 73 (Stillwell P 968)
A:— 1; 6: throughout.
B:— 1; 4; 5: straight; 6: with stems.
C:— 1: 1; 2: 7; 3: 4; 4: red; 5; 7a.
D:— 1: C and F ♭, ♱ or ♒ ; 2: ✓ ; 3: bars between sentences.

HYMNARIUM
Murcia: P. Brun and J. Gentil, s.a.
Oxf. Bodl. Inc. b. S. 97.1
Boh. 709
A:— 5.
D:— 4: 2 leaves, text and short commentary.

HYMNARIUM
Paris: Caillaut, 1492
Cambridge UL., Oates 2938
Boh. 713
A:— 5.
D:— 4: aurea expositio hymnorum cum textu.

HYMNARIUM (HYMNI)
Paris: Levet, 1487
Cambridge UL., Oates 2981
Boh. 712?
A:— 5.
D:— 4: aurea expositio hymnorum cum textu; perhaps erroneously ascribed by Bohatta to Vérard, 1498, an edition which could not be located at Oxford.

HYMNI
Tarragona: Rosenbach, 1498
Stillwell E 125
Boh. 717; Haebler 252
= Expositiones; listed in GK. as Hymni.

HYMNI
Zaragossa: Hurus, *c.* 1500

Stillwell E 126
Haebler 255
= Expositiones.

23. LIBER CATECHUMENI
Venice: Spira, 1500
Stillwell L 172
Boh. 726
A:— 1; 6: throughout.
B:— 1; 3: ⌐ and ⌐ ♒ ◫ ◪ ♒ ♜, ⌐ for beginning and end; some parts 4; 5: straight, no points; 6: with stems.
C:— 1: 1; 2: 6; 3: 4; 4: red; 5; 7a.
D:— 1: C and F ♭ ♒ ; 2: ✓ ; 3: bars at end of sentences, printed in same procedure with the notes; 4: ornamented initials; frontispiece woodcut with scenes of baptism, the priest holding a book in his hands.

LIBER CATECHUMENI
Florence: Alopa, 1496
Stillwell L 171
A:— 5.
D:— 4: this book is a regular Agenda, beginning with the rites of baptism.

LITANIE AMBROSIANE
Milan: Ungardus, 1476
Br.M. IA. 26931
A:— 5.

LITANIE AMBROSIANE
Milan: Zarotus, 1494
Paris BN. Rés. B. 1687
Paris Maz. 764 cat., p. 401
A:— 5.
D:— 4: the rubrics in Italian, otherwise Latin text. In the catalogue of the Mazarine the book is called Processionale.

24. MAGNIFICAT
Milan: Zarotus, 1486
Br.M. IB. 26533
Stillwell P 968
Boh. 945; Proctor 5819a
A:— 4; 6: on fol. 2a 5 places, on fol. 2b 2 places are left free for staves; both copies bound together with Psalterium Ambrosianum, Milan: Pachel and Scinzenzeler, 1486.

MANUALE BURGENSE
Zaragossa: Hurus, 1497
Br.M. IB. 52193
Haebler 394

A:— 5.

D:— 4: title: Incipit manuale sive practica ministrandi sacramenta: cum missis votivis.

MANUALE CAESARAUGUSTA-NUM
Hijar: Cordoba, *c.* 1486
Stillwell M 184
Haebler 394 (5)

A:— 5.

D:— 4: title: Manuale sive practica ministrandi sacramenta; incipit benedictio aque. Ornamented title-border in double print; Spanish text on fol. n2.

25. MANUALE CARNOTENSE
    (CHARTRES)
Paris: Maynial pro Remyl, 1490
Paris BN. Rés. B. 2954
Boh. 728

A:— 1 before and 2 following the Canon; 6: Dom. Ramis—Benedictio Fontis—Finis.

B:— 1: 1; 3: type similar to the following item, but not identical; 5: without points; 6: stems occasionally.

C:— 1: 1 before, and 2 following the Canon; 2: 8; 3: 4; 4: red; 5; 7a before the Canon; following the Canon probably 7c.

D:— 1: C and F 𝄢 8 𝄢; 2: none; 3: bars separating words; 4: this edition seems to have been a kind of model for the following item.

26. MANUALE CARNOTENSE
Paris: Higman, 1500
Paris BN. Rés. B. 1752

A:— 1; 6: Dom. Ramis—Benedictio fontis—Finis.

B:— 1: 1; 3: ♮ ♮ ♮ ♮; 5: slightly curved; 6: no stems.

C:— 1: 1; 2: 8; 3: 4; 4: red; 5; 7a, with pieces of identical length.

D:— 1: C and F 𝄢 ♩ 8; 2: ♩ occasionally; 3: bars separating words; 4: typical Parisian style.

27. MANUALE CONSTANTIENSE
    (COUTANCES)
Rouen: Le Bourgeois, 1494
Paris BN. Rés. B. 1791
Paris Maz. 778, cat., p. 409
Boh. 730

A:— 2 in the BN. copy; 4 in the Maz. copy; 6: throughout.

(B:— 2 MS. in the BN. copy; 1 MS. in the Maz. copy.)

C:— 1: 1; 2: 8; 3: 4; 4: red; 5; 7c in the BN. copy; in the Maz. copy initials and staves in MS., drawn apparently with a raster.

D:— 4: printer's sign at beginning and end; Lit.: J. L. Adam, 'Le Manuel de Coutances' in *Rev. cathol. de Normandie*, vols. 18/19, 1909/10.

MANUALE DIVINUM
Venice: de Vitalibus, s.a.
Stillwell M 186

A:— 5.

D:— 4: Manuale divinum ex sacrarum litterarum viridario delectum in quo continentur . . . . Commentary on the letters of St. Paul.

MANUALE HISPALENSE
Seville: Ungut and Polonus, 1494
Br.M. IA. 52369
Boh. 731; Haebler 395

A:— 5.

MANUALE LAUSANNENSE
Geneva: Belot, 1500
Br.M. IA. 38478
Boh. 733

A:— 5.

D:— 4: woodcut on title—Tabula manualis (2 pp.)—woodcut; bound together with Weale 492, manc.; many leaves with prayers in Latin, German, and French in MS. added.

28. MANUALE NANNETENSE
    (NANTES)
Paris: Le Blanc, *c.* 1495
Paris BN. Rés. B. 1815

A:— 1; 6: throughout.

B:— 1; 3: ♮ ♮ ♮ ♮ ♮; 5: straight; 6: no stems.

C:— 1: 1; 2: 6; 3: 4; 4: red; 5; 7a, with pieces of identical length.

D:— 1: C and F 𝄢, 8 𝄢; 2: ✓; 3: bars to separate words: 4: colophon 'Veneunt Nannetis apud Mathurium Papolin et Gabrielem Le Blanc'.

29. MANUALE PARISIENSE
Paris: Morand, 1497
Paris SG. OE. 15.681, cat. 854
Boh. 735
A:— 1; 6: throughout.
B:— 1: 1; 3: ꝗ ꝑ �; 5: straight; 6: no stems.
C:— 1: 1; 2: 8; 3: 4; 4: red; 5; 7a, pieces of different lengths.
D:— 1: C and F ♭ ♮ 8; 2: none; 3: bars separating words.

The MANUALE PAROCHIALIUM SACERDOTUM is not a liturgical book; editions and copies verified:
Augsburg: Kästlin, 1484
Br.M.; Bodl. Auct. 7 Q. 7. 15; Stillwell M 187
Augsburg: Froschauer, 1499
Br.M.; Bodl. Auct. 7 Q. 7. 5; Stillwell M 192
Cologne: Quentell, c. 1489
Br.M.; Paris SG. OE. 15; Stillwell M 188
Cologne: Quentell, 1492 (?)
Br.M.; Stillwell M 191
Leipzig: Kachelofen, 1489 (?)
Br.M.; Stillwell M 190
Reutlingen: Otmar, s.a.
Br.M. IA. 10729
Strasbourg: Printer of the *Vitae Patrum*, 1485 (?)
Br.M.; Stillwell M 189

MANUALE SARUM
Rouen: Olivier and Joh. de Lorraine, 1501
Oxf. Bodl. Douce 152
Bohatta 740 lists this edition as of 1500; not in Proctor; in Frère, *Des livres de liturgie*, 1867, and in colophon 1501.

30. MANUALE SENONENSE
Paris: Hopyl, 1500 (?)
Paris SG. OE. B. B. 4° 207, cat. 1041
Boh. 741
A:— 1; 6: throughout.
B:— 1; 3: ꝛune ꝗ% ꝶ ꝶ; 5: straight; 6: no stems.
C:— 1: 1; 2: 7; 3: 4; 4: red; 5; 7a, pieces of different lengths.
D:— 1: C and F ♭ ♮ 8; 2: none; 3: bars separating words; 4: Manuale seu instructorium . . . Impensis symonis vostre.

31. MANUALE TULLENSE
Bamberg?: Sensenschmidt?, s.a.
Paris BN. Rés. B. 1818

A:— 4; 6: in officio mortuorum.
C:— 1: 1; 2: 5.
D:— 4: in old handwriting 'Manuale sive Rituale ad usum ecclesie Tullensis. Bamberg. Sensenschmidt'.

32. MISSALE ABOENSE
Lübeck: Ghotan, 1488
*Oxf. Bodl. and Cambridge UL., one leaf each in Klemming, *Sveriges äldre liturgiska literatur; Weale 1*
A:— 4; 6: before and in the Canon.
C:— 1: 1 in the Canon, two before the Canon; 2: 11.
D:— 4: staves with 4 red lines drawn by hand; description supplemented from the copy in the Royal Library at Stockholm.

33. MISSALE AMBIANENSE (AMIENS)
Paris: s. typ., 1487
Paris BN. Rés. B. 766
Weale 12
A:— 2; 6: before and in the Canon.
C:— 1: 2; 2: 8; 3: 4; 4: red; 5; 7b.
D:— 4: several coloured woodcuts.

34. MISSALE AMBROSIANUM
Milan: Zarotus, 1475
Paris BN. Rés. B. 1485
Weale 26; Lib. 14
A:— 4: (lines and music in MS.); among the 6 lines of the staves the yellow line for C and the red line for F are so evenly drawn that they almost look printed; 6: before and in the Canon.
C:— 1: 2; 2: 8.

35. MISSALE AMBROSIANUM
Milan: Valdarfer (Christ. Ratisponensis), 1482
Paris SG. OE. 15.150, cat. 361
Weale 27
A:— 1; 6: before and in the Canon.
B:— 1, 1a; 3: ꝶ ∾ ∞; 5: straight, with points for the lunga and the ligatures; 6: both forms ○ ♮ ∾ ꝺ.
C:— 1: 2; 2: 8; 3: 4; 4: red; 5; 7c.
D:— 1: C and F ♭ ‖ between the lines; 2: ꝺ; 3: bars separating words; 4: the form of the notes imitating neumes; a second copy on smaller paper.

36. MISSALE AMBROSIANUM
Milan: Pachel, 1499
Paris SG. OE. 15.698, cat. 934
Weale 33

A:— 1; 6: before and in the Canon.
B:— 2; 3: ↶ ↶: 5; curved, with points;
6: both forms, ◦ ⅃.
C:— 1: 2; 2: 10; 3: 4; 4: red; 5; 7a, pieces
of equal length.
D:— 1: C and F ℭ ‖; 2: ✓; 3: bars separating
words; 4: the forms of the notes imitating
neumes, similar, but not identical with preceding number; facs. Molitor, pl. 19.

37. MISSALE ANDEGAVENSE
(ANGERS)
Paris: Higman and Hopyl, 1489
Br.M. IB. 40106
Paris SG. OE. 15.598, cat. 544
Weale 55
A:— 1 before, 1 and 3 in, and 3 after the
Canon.
B:— 1; 3: ♭ ♭ ♮ ♭♭; 4: mostly; 5: slightly
curved, without points; 6: no stems.
C:— 1: 2; 2: 10; 3: 4; 4: red; 5; 7a.
D:— 1: C and F ♭ ⅃ 8; 2: none; 3: bars
separating words; 4: after the calendar two
woodcuts; following fol. s4 starts the sec-
tion with music, A⁸–B⁸; the text, then,
starts with 'A' again; of this part the first
leaves only are numbered Fo 1–Fo xviii; on
fol. B8v 'Anthienne et oraison de la vierge
marie'; otherwise rubrics in Latin.

38. MISSALE AQUILEIENSE
Augsburg: Ratdolt, 1494
Stillwell M 553
Weale 79
A:— 1; 6: throughout.
B:— 2; 3: ◦♭ ♫ ♪; 4: numerous; 6: both
forms.
C:— 1: 1; 2: 9; 3: 4; 4: red; 6: a, d(2); 7a.
D:— 1: C and F ℭ ♯; 2: ∿; 3: bars sepa-
rating sentences; 4: coloured woodcuts in
dedication and before Canon.

39. MISSALE ARGENTINENSE
Strasbourg: Pruess, c. 1490
Paris BN. Rés. B. 1496
Weale 88

A:— 1; 6: before the Canon, 9 fols. inserted,
and in the Canon.
B:— 2; 3: ◁ ⌂; 6: ⎮ and ∿, both forms
used for one and the same word.
C:— 1: 1; 2: 8; 3: 4; 4: red; 6: a, d(2); 7b.
D:— 1: F ⅃; 2: ∿; 4: forms very similar to
Wenssler's.

40. MISSALE AUGUSTENSE
Augsburg: Ratdolt, 1496
Stillwell M 554
Weale 105
A:— 1; 6: before the Canon, fols. c–cxii, and
'credo in unum deum' on fol. cxii, vellum,
belonging to the Canon gathering.
B:— 2; 3: ◦♭ ♪ ◦♭◦; 6: ⎮ to indicate accent.
C:— 1: 1; 2: 9; 3: 4; 4: red; 6: a, d(2); 7a.
D:— 1: C and F ℭ ♯ one beneath the other
in the border, ♭ in the stave; 2: ✓; 3: black
bars at the end of the stave, if it ends inside
a row; 4: 2 woodcuts in five-colour print;
initials and printer's sign in red and black.

41. MISSALE AUTISSIODORENSE
(AUXERRE)
Paris: Dupré, 1490
Paris SG. OE. 15. B. B., fol. 140, in none of
the printed catalogues
Weale 124
A:— 4; 6: before the Canon which is missing.
C:— 1: 2; 2: 8.

42. MISSALE BAMBERGENSE
Bamberg: Sensenschmidt and Petzen-
steiner, 1490
Br.M. IC. 2638
Paris BN. Rés. Vél. 211
Weale 130; Lib. 15
A:— 1; 6: before the Canon.
B:— 2; 3: ♏ ♪; 4: frequently; 5: straight;
6: stems to indicate the beginning of a word.
C:— 1: 1; 2: 10; 3: 4; 4: red; 6: a, d(2); 7b(c?).
D:— 1: C and F ℭ ♭, one sign beneath the
other; 2: ◊; 3: bars separating words;
4: Canon on vellum.

43. MISSALE BAMBERGENSE
Bamberg: Pfeyl, 1499
Paris BN. Rés. B. 779
Stillwell M 555
Weale 132
A:— 1; 6: Canon missing; 15 unnumbered

leaves with music are inserted between fol. 131 'hec servanda sunt scdm. ordinem eccl. Babenbergensis', and fol. 164.

B:— 2; 3: ♪ ♪ ♪; 5: straight; 6: with stems to indicate the beginning of a word.

C:— 1: 1; 2: 10; 3: 4; 4: red; 6: a, d(2); 7a, pieces of identical length.

D:— 1: C and F ℭ ꝯ, one sign beneath the other, ♭; 2: ✓; 3: bars separating words; 4: the section with music printed apparently separately, but in the same shop.

44. MISSALE BASILIENSE (CONSTAN-TIENSE)
   Basle: Wenssler, *c.* 1480
   Stillwell M 556
   Weale 153

A:— 4; 6: before and after the Canon (fols. 263/4).

C:— 1: 2; 2: 9.

D:— 4: *Gutenberg-Jahrbuch*, 1935, p. 118, no. 7.

45. MISSALE BASILIENSE
   Basle: Richel, 1480
   Oxf. Bodl. Auct. 6. Q. II. 19
   Weale 154

A:— 4; 6: before, in, and after the Canon.

C:— 1: 2; 2: 9 before and after, 6 in, the Canon.

D:— 4: Lit.: A. Pfister, 'Vom frühsten Musik-druck in der Schweiz', in *Festschrift Gustav Binz zum 70. Geburtstag*, 1935.

46. MISSALE BASILIENSE
   Basle: Wenssler, ante 1485
   Cambridge UL., Oates 2752
   Weale 155

A:— 4: 6: before and in the Canon.

C:— 1: 1, and 2 on fol. 85b only; 2: 8 before and 10 in the Canon.

D:— 4: copy manc.: *Gutenberg-Jahrbuch*, 1935, p. 118, no. 8.

   MISSALE BASILIENSE
   Basle: Wenssler(?), *c.* 1485
   Stillwell M 557
   Weale 156(?)

A:— 5.

D:— 4: this copy in the Union Theological Seminary, New York, is manc.; it is doubtful whether this missal was printed by Wenssler.

47. MISSALE BASILIENSE
   Basle: Wenssler, 1488
   Br.M. IB. 37136
   Weale 158; Lib. 16

A:— 4; 6: before and in the Canon.

C:— 1: 2 before and 1 in the Canon; 2: 10 before and 7 in the Canon.

D:— 4: Sequentiale at end; MS. insertions in an old hand; *Gutenberg-Jahrbuch*, 1935, p. 118, no. 20.

   MISSALE BASILIENSE
   Basle: Wenssler, 1494
   Paris BN. Rés. B. 1480
   Weale 159

A:— 5.

D:— 4: *Gutenberg-Jahrbuch*, 1935, p. 118, no. 33.

   MISSALE BISUNTINENSE (BESANÇON)
   Salins: Bigot, Bodram, and Dupré, 1485
   Paris BN. Rés. B. 1350
   Weale 174

A:— 5.

48. MISSALE BISUNTINENSE
   Paris: Dupré, 1497
   Paris BN. Rés. Vél. 155
   Weale 175

A:— 2; 6: before and in the Canon.

C:— 1: 2; 2: 13; 3: 4; 4: red; 5; 7b(c?).

D:— 4: the MS. notes are written so regularly that they look printed, but the ink is faded.

49. MISSALE BRACARENSE
   Lisbon: Saxonia, 1498
   Stillwell M 560
   Weale 196; Haebler 440

A:— 3; 6: before and in the Canon.

C:— 1: 2; 2: 8; 3: 4; 4: red; 5; 7b, staves printed obviously together with rubrics, probably metal.

50. MISSALE BRIXINENSE
   Augsburg: Ratdolt, 1493
   Br.M. IB. 6740
   Cambridge UL., Oates 964
   Paris BN. Rés. Vél. 791
   Stillwell M 561
   Weale 206; Lib. 17

A:— 1; 6: before and in the Canon.

B:— 2; 3: ♪ ♪; 5: small points; 6: stems occasionally to indicate beginning of word.

C:— 1: 1; 2: 8 before and 7 in the Canon; 3: 4; 4: red; 5; 7a, pieces of different lengths.

D:— 1: C and F 𝄢 𝄢; 2: ∾; 3: bars separating sentences, occasionally; 4: facsimile of music in Schottenloher, pl. 21.

51. MISSALE CABILONENSE (CHALON s. S.)
Lyons: Boninis, 1500
Paris BN. Rés. B. 147
Weale 213

A:— 1; 6: suppl. 28 leaves, fol. cccv–cccxxxij.

B:— 1; 3: ♩ ♭ ♩⁊; 5: straight; 6: no stems.

C:— 1: 2; 2: 10; 3: 4; 4: red; 5; 7a, pieces of different lengths.

D:— 1: C and F ꜙ ⁊ꜙ, ♭♮; 2: ♮; 3: bars separating words.

52. MISSALE CAESARAUGUSTANUM (OSCENSE)
Zaragossa: Hurus, 1488
Stillwell M 580
Haebler 447 (441)
Weale 691

A:— 2; 6: before the Canon, fols. 191a–8b.

C:— 1: 1; 2: 7; 3: 4; 4: red; 5; 7c(?).

D:— 4: Lit.: Haebler in *Zentralblatt*, 1909, p. 154, and in *Bibliogr. Iberica*. The missal was first printed in 1485 for Zaragossa; as it did not sell, the copies were rebound and changed into missals for Huesca in 1488.

53. MISSALE CAMERACENSE (CAMBRAI)
Paris: Higman, 1495
Paris BN. Rés. Vél. 156
Weale 226

A:— 3; 6: before and after the Canon.

C:— 1: 1; 2: 7; 3: 4; 4: red; 5; 7b.

D:— 4: MS. notes on staves of three and four lines written very carefully; staves of different width.

54. MISSALE CARNOTENSE (CHARTRES)
Chartres: Dupré, 1482
Paris BN. Rés. Vél. 790
Weale 234

A:— 2; 6: before and in the Canon.

C:— 1: 2; 2: 10; 3: 4; 4: red; 5; 7b.

55. MISSALE CARNOTENSE
Paris: Higman, 1490
Paris Ars. 4° T 846
Weale 236

A:— 1; 6: before and in the Canon.

B:— 1; 3: ♭♩; 4: mostly; 5: curved, no points; 6: no stems.

C:— 1: 2; 2: 10; 3: 4; 4: red; 5; 7a, with sections so small as to suggest single-type printing.

D:— 1: C and F ꜙ ⁊ꜙ 8, ♭; 2: none; 3: bars separating words; 4: coloured Canon picture on vellum.

56. MISSALE CATHALAUNENSE (CHALONS s. M.)
Paris: Dupré, 1489
Paris BN. Rés. Vél. 157
Weale 253

A:— 2; 6: after the Canon.

C:— 1: 2; 2: 8; 3: 4; 4: red; 5; 7b(c?).

D:— 4: richly illuminated; MS. notes rather carelessly written.

57. MISSALE CENOMANENSE (LE MANS)
Paris: Higman, 1494
Paris SG. OE. 15. 650, cat. 731
Weale 260

A:— 1; 6: before and in the Canon.

B:— 1; 3: ♭ ⁊♩ ♮⁊; 5: curved, no points; 6: no stems.

C:— 1: 2; 2: 10; 3: 4; 4: red; 5; 7a, pieces of different lengths.

D:— 1: C and F ꜙ ⁊ꜙ 8; 2: none; 3: bars separating words; 4: edit. per petrum hennier; MS. initials.

58. MISSALE CLAROMONTENSE (CLERMONT-FERRAND)
Venice: Birreta, 1492
Paris Ars. 8° T. 2141
Weale 277

A:— 4; 6: before and in the Canon.

C:— 1: 2; 2: 8.

D:— 4: this missal differs from the following; in the Arsenal copy the staves are set in 2 columns; in the Mazarine copy they stretch over the whole leaf in the Canon. Delisle is right in attributing the latter copy to Topié in Lyons; see note for following item.

59. MISSALE CLAROMONTENSE
Lyons: Topié, *c. 1494*
Paris Maz. XV. 693, cat. p. 360
Weale 277 (!)
A:— 4; 6: before and in the Canon.
C:— 1: 2 before, one and two in the Canon;
2: 8.
D:— 4: the exact title is: Ordo missalis;
Weale quotes the title, &c., from the
Mazarine catalogue as printed 'Ven. Birreta,
1492'. In the copy of the catalogue in the
reading-room of the Mazarine, as well as in
the copy of the book itself, this statement
is corrected by the hand of Delisle. The
source for Delisle is: A. Tardieu, *Histoire
généalogique de Clermont-Ferrand*, vol. ii.

60. MISSALE COLONIENSE
Cologne: Homborch, 1481
Paris BN. Rés. B. 801
Weale 286
Voulliéme 801
A:— 4; 6: before and in the Canon.
C:— 1: 2; 2: 11.
D:— 4: MS. notes and staves written very
carelessly.

61. MISSALE COLONIENSE
Basle: Wenssler, 1487
Oxf. Bodl. Auct. VI. Q. I. 15
Weale 288
A:— 4; 6: before and in the Canon.
C:— 1: 1 in, 2 before the Canon; 2: 10.
D:— 4: *Gutenberg-Jahrbuch*, 1935, p. 118,
no. 13.

62. MISSALE COLONIENSE
Cologne: Quentell, 1494
Paris BN. Rés. B. 802
Weale 289
Voulliéme 903
A:— 1: 2 and 3 before, 4 in the Canon; 6:
before and in the Canon.
C:— 1: 2; 2: 10; 3: 4; 4: red; 5; 7c(b?).

63. MISSALE COLONIENSE
Cologne: Bungart, 1498
Paris BN. Rés. B. 804
*Wells College, Aurora, U.S.A. (not in
Stillwell)*
Weale 290; Voulliéme 804
A:— 4; 6: before and in the Canon.
C:— 1: 2; 2: 14 before, 10 in the Canon.

D:— 4: in Paris copy notes written very
neatly.

64. MISSALE CONSTANTIENSE
Basle: Richel, before 1481
Stillwell M 562
Weale 306
A:— 1; 6: before and in the Canon.
B:— 2; 3: ¶ ⋔, not frequently; 5: ⋌ small
points; 6: both forms, almost alternating.
C:— 1: 2; 2: 9 before and 7 in the Canon,
with the same space between the lines, but
the staves set more apart; 3: 4; 4: red;
6: a, d(1); 7b.
D:— 1: C and F ⋒ ⋩; 2: ⋌; 3: no bars;
4: not mentioned in Pfister's bibliography,
see note to Weale 154.

65. MISSALE CONSTANTIENSE
Basle: Kollicker, 1485
Br.M. IC. 37568
Oxf. Bodl. frg.
Stillwell M 563
Weale 307; Lib. 18
A:— 4; 6: before and in the Canon.
C:— 1: 1; 2: 11 before and 10 in the Canon.

MISSALE CRACOVIENSE
Mainz: Peter Schoeffer, 1484
Stillwell M 564
Weale 326
A:— 5.

66. MISSALE EBROICENSE (ÉVREUX)
Paris: Dupré, 1492
Stillwell M 565
Weale 365
A:— 4; 6: before the Canon which is missing
in the Huntington copy.
C:— 1: 2; 2: 9.
D:— 4: the staves are obviously drawn by a
raster; the colour differs from initials, and
the lines of the staves do not start or end at
the same point; several illuminated wood-
cuts in the text.

67. MISSALE EBROICENSE
Rouen: Morin, 1497
Paris SG. OE. 15. 477, cat. 842
Paris Ars. f. T. 688
Weale 366
A:— 2; 6: before and in the Canon.
C:— 1: 2; 2: 13; 3: 4; 4: red; 5; 7b.

68. MISSALE EDUENSE (AUTUN)
Paris: Higman, 1493
Paris BN. Rés. B. 144
Paris SG. OE. 15. 158, cat. 686
Weale 375
A:— 1; 6: throughout.
B:— 1; 3: ♭ 🎵 🎵 🎵 🎵; 5: slightly curved,
no points; 6: stems to indicate end of words.
C:— 1: 2; 2: 10; 3: 4; 4: red; 5; 7a, pieces of
identical lengths.
D:— 1: C and F ⟦ ⟧ 8; 2: none; 3: bars
separating words.

MISSALE EYSTETENSE
(EICHSTÄDT)
Eichstädt: Reyser, 1486
Paris BN. Rés. Vel. 218
Weale 388
A:— 5.
D:— 4: long printed introduction with the
coat of arms in woodcut; MS. notes on the
white leaf before the Canon.

69. MISSALE FRISINGENSE
Bamberg: Sensenschmidt, 1487
Br.M. IC. 2634
Stillwell M 566 frg.
Weale 395; Lib. 19
A:— 1; 6: 21 leaves before the Canon, and
5 staves on back of Canon part.
B:— 2; 3: 🎵 🎵; 4: frequently, e.g. ◦ 🎵;
5: straight; 6: no stems.
C:— 1: 1, and 2 on the back of Canon part;
2: 10; 3: 4; 4: red; 6: a, d(2); 7b.
D:— 1: C and F ℭ 🎵; 2: ◇; 3: bars separat-
ing sentences.

70. MISSALE FRISINGENSE
Augsburg: Ratdolt, 1492
Br.M. IB. 6727
Paris BN. Rés. B. 28984
Weale 396; Lib. 20
A:— 1; 6: before the Canon.
B:— 2; 3: 🎵 🎵 🎵; 4: frequently; 5: straight,
points on top and bottom of ligatures; 6: no
stems.
C:— 1: 1; 2: 8; 3: 4; 4: red; 5; 7a.
D:— 1: C and F ℭ 🎵; 2: ✓ only occasion-
ally; 3: bars separating words.

71. MISSALE GEBENNENSE (GENEVA)
Geneva: Fabri, 1491
Paris BN. Rés. b. 266
Weale 401
A:— 2; and 3.
C:— 1: 2; 2: 10; 3: 4; 4: red; 5; 7b.
D:— 4: Manc., missing leaves in facsimile;
MS. notes very carefully written.

72. MISSALE GIENNENSE (JAÉN)
Seville: Ungut, 1499
Stillwell M 567
Weale 406
A:— 1 and 3; before and in the Canon.
B:— 1; 3: ♭ 🎵 🎵 🎵; 5: straight ♮;
6: no stems.
C:— 1: 2; 2: 9; 3: 4; 4: red; 5; 7c.
D:— 1: F 🎵🎵; 2: ✓; 3: bars between words,
they are sometimes double and threefold at
the end of a line.

73. MISSALE HALBERSTADTENSE
Augsburg: Ratdolt, 1490
Stillwell M 568
Weale 417
A:— 1 and 3; 6: 1 before and 3 in the Canon.
B:— 2; 3: 🎵 🎵; mostly 4; 5: straight; 6:
stems only to designate beginning words 🎵.
C:— 1: 1; 2: 9; 3: 4; 4: red; 6: a, d(2); 7a.
D:— 1: C and F 🎵 ℭ; 2: ✓; 3: none; 4:
Canon on vellum.

74. MISSALE HALBERSTADTENSE
Strasbourg: Grüninger, *c.* 1500
(Canon, Mainz: Schoeffer)
Oxf. Bodl. Auct. VI. Q. I. 23
Weale 418
Stillwell M 569
A:— 1; 6: before and in the Canon, and 2
fols. at the end 'Et quia in paucis ecclesiis in
diocesi halberstatensi servatur debitus accen-
tus in his sequentibus, ut ergo sit concordia
ista hic notata sunt'.
B:— 2; 3: 🎵 🎵 🎵; 4: single note ◇ and
🎵 or 🎵.
C:— 1: 1; 2: 11; 3: 4; 4: red; 5; 7c(?).
D:— 1: C and F 🎵 🎵, ♭; 2: none; 3: bars
occasionally; 4: the musical appendix sup-
plies the tunes for the lections.

75. MISSALE HERBIPOLENSE
Würzburg: Reyser, 1481
Oxf. Bodl. Auct. I. Q. 17
Weale 428
A:— 1; 6: 21 leaves directly before the Canon.
B:— 2; 3: ♩ ♫ ◦ ♪; mostly 4; 6: with stems.
C:— 1: 1; 2: 11; 3: 4; 4: red; 6: d(1); 7c.
D:— 1: C and F ℭ ♪, ♭; 2: ✗; 3: bars to separate sentences; 4: copy on vellum, in front of the printed part with music, one leaf handwritten music as well as text; also MS. initials for Kyrie and Gloria; Facs. Molitor, pls. 3/4, and Riemann, pl. 17.

76. MISSALE HERBIPOLENSE
Würzburg: Reyser, 1484
Br.M. IC. 10511
Weale 430; Lib. 21
A:— 1; 6: 18 leaves inserted before the Canon, and 4, in the Canon.
B:— 2; 3: ♩ ♫; 4: frequently; 6: with stems.
C:— 1: 1; 2: 12; 3: 4; 4: red; 6: a, d(1); 7b.
D:— 1: C and F ℭ ♪, ♭; 2: ✗; 3: bars separating sentences.

77. MISSALE HERBIPOLENSE
Würzburg: Reyser, 1491
Paris BN. Rés. Vél. 237
Weale 432
A:— 1; 6: 18 leaves with music are inserted before the Canon, that is in the so-called 'canon minor'.
B:— 2; 3: ♩ ♫ ; 4: frequently; 6: mostly ♪.
C:— 1: 1; 2: 12; 3: 4; 4: red; 6: a, d(1); 7b.
D:— 1: C and F ℭ ♪, ♭; 2: ✗; 3: bars between words; 4: *édition de luxe*.

78. MISSALE HERBIPOLENSE
Würzburg: Reyser, 1493
Paris BN. Rés. Vél. 238
Stillwell M 570
Weale 433
A–C, see Weale 432.
D:— 4: almost identical with the previous item no. 77; only minor differences in the order of the notes, in the type of the numbering, &c.; two further leaves added at the beginning of the part with music from another edition, '*c.* 1490', probably Weale 430; one of these leaves with music 'Kyrie'.

MISSALE SPECIALE HERBIPOLENSE
Würzburg: Reyser, 1495
Br.M. IB. 10519
Cambridge UL., Oates 1205
Paris BN. Rés. B. 275
Stillwell M 571
Weale 434; Lib. 22
A:— 5.

79. MISSALE HILDENSEMENSE
Nuremberg: Stuchs, 1499
Br.M. IB. 8116
Weale 447; Lib. 23
A:— 1; 6: fols. 183–240, beginning with 'In festo Purificationis Marie'.
B:— 2; 3: the setting of the music differs in the four sections starting at fols. 183, 199, 203, and 217 resp.; the settings in sections 1 and 3 are identical, and have no ligatures; ligatures in section 2 ♩ ♩ ♫ ◦ ♪; ligatures in section 4 ♩ ♫ ◦ ♪; in sections 1 and 3: 4; 5: straight, no points, ♪ for liquescens; 6: no stems in sections 1 and 3, both forms in section 2.
C:— 1: 1; 2: 8 and 9; 3: 4 and 5; 4: red; 6: a, d(2); 7c.
D:— 1: in sections 1 and 3 C ℇ, in section 2 C and F ℇ ♭, in section 4 C and F ℭ ♪; 2: ✗; bars between sentences.

80. MISSALE HILDENSEMENSE
Nuremberg: Stuchs, 1499
Stillwell M 572
variant
A:— 1; 6: 16 leaves inserted between Calendar and the first numbered folio; and 18 leaves between fols. 174 and 175.
B:— 2; 3: ♫ ♩ ◦ ♪ ♪ ◦; 5: straight, no points, and ♪ for liquescens; 6: no stems.
C:— 1: 1; 2: 8; 3: 4; 4: red; 6: a, d(2).
D:— 1: C and F ℇ ♭; 2: ✗; 3: bars between sentences.

MISSALE ITINERANTIUM
Cologne: M. de Werden, 1499
Cambridge UL., Oates 850
Weale 459; Voulliéme 805
A:— 5.
D:— 4: subtitle 'Misse peculiares . . . de dulcissimo nomine Jesu officium. . . . de tribus magis per iter agentibus officium . . . .'.

15

Chief title 'Evagatorium'; attributed by Voulliéme to Quentell, *c.* 1500.

MISSALE ITINERANTIUM
Cologne: Quentell, 1500
Oxf. Bodl. Mason JJ. 496
Weale 460; Voulliéme 806
A:— 5.
D:— 4: small 8°.

81. MISSALE LAUDUNENSE (LAON)
Paris: Dupré, 1491
Paris Ars. f. T. 689
Weale 483
A:— 4; 6: before, that is on the verso of the Canon picture, and in the Canon.
C:— 1: 2; 2: 10.

82. MISSALE LAUSANNENSE
(LAUSANNE)
Lausanne: Belot, 1493
Paris BN. Rés. B. 1472
Weale 491
A:— 2; 6: before the Canon; the leaves for the Canon are left white, and the Canon is added in MS. at the end on vellum.
C:— 1: 1; 2: 8; 3: 4; 4: red; 5; 7c.

MISSALE LAUSANNENSE
Geneva: Belot, 1500
Br.M. IA. 38479
Weale 492
A:— 5.
D:— 4: incomplete parts from a missal: Veni mecum—in die nativitatis. Apparently sections from a Missale Itinerantium, see MS. note in copy; bound together with 'Manuale ad usum lausannensem'.

83. MISSALE LEMOVICENSE
(LIMOGES)
Limoges: Berton, 1500
Paris BN. Rés. Vel. 1606
Weale 498
A:— 2 and 3; 6: before and in the Canon.
C:— 1: 1, against the general text in two columns; 2: 7 and 8; 3: 4; 4: red; 5; 7b.

84. MISSALE LEODIENSE (LIÉGE)
Delft: Snellaert, *c.* 1495
Paris BN. Rés. B. 816
Paris Maz. 445, cat. p. 231
Weale 510
A:— 3; 6: before and in the Canon.
C:— 1: 2; 2: 11; 3: 4; 4: black; 5; 7b(c?).

85. MISSALE LEODIENSE
Paris: Higman, 1499
Paris BN. Rés. Vél. 219
Stillwell M 573
Weale 511
A:— 1, 2, and 3; 6: 1 before, 2 and 3 in the Canon.
B:— 1; 3: ♩ ♭ ♯; 5: curved, small points; 6: no stems.
C:— 1: 2; 2: 10; 3: 4; 4: red; 5; 7a, pieces of identical length.
D:— 1: C and F ♩ or 〔 ♩ 〕 8; 2: none; 3: bars separating words.

MISSALE LINGONENSE (LANGRES)
Paris: Dupré, 1491
Br.M. IB. 39833
Weale 535
A:— 5.

86. MISSALE LUGDUNENSE
Lyons: Numeister, 1487
Paris BN. Rés. Vél. 164
Weale 546
A:— 2 before and 4 in the Canon.
C:— 1: 1; 2: 7; 3: 4; 4: red; 5; 7b.
D:— 4: the numbering of the leaves in the Canon, part of the text, initials, and borders in MS.; the red lines of the staves sometimes running over the initials.

MISSALE MAGDEBURGENSE
Magdeburg: M. Brandis, 1480
Br.M. IC. 10902
Cambridge UL., Oates 1225 (?)
Stillwell M 574
Weale 569; Lib. 24
A:— 5.
D:— 4: Stillwell and the Cambridge cat. give as typ. Ghotan.

MISSALE MAGDEBURGENSE
Magdeburg: Koch, 1486
Br.M. IC. 10932
Paris BN. Rés. B. 824
Stillwell M 575
Weale 570; Lib. 25
A:— 5.

MISSALE MAGDEBURGENSE
Lübeck: M. Brandis, 1493

Oxf. Bodl. Auct. 6. Q. infra II. 23
Weale 572
A:— 5.
D:— 4: ornamented initials; Canon missing.

MISSALE MAGDEBURGENSE
Magdeburg: M. Brandis, 1497
Br.M. IC. 10957
Stillwell M 576
Weale 573; Lib. 26
A:— 5.
D:— 4: in the copy in the Huntington Lib., no. 17860, 14 leaves with MS. music inserted before the Canon, and 6 leaves before the Commune Sanctorum; bound together with Sequentiarium, texts only, in a completely different type; this part is listed as Registrum Hamburgense in the Huntington catalogue.

87. MISSALE MOGUNTINUM
    (MAGUNTINENSE)
    Würzburg: Reyser, 1482
    Br.M. IC. 10506
    Weale 622; Lib. 27
A:— 1; 6: before and in the Canon.
B:— 2; 3: 𝄢, otherwise 4; 5: straight, with points; 6: both forms.
C:— 1: 1; 2: 11; 3: 4; 4: red; 6: a, d(1); 7b.
D:— 1: C and F 𝄢 ✓ or 𝄈; 2: no guides; 3: there is a vertical end stroke; 4: in the Canon the staves are partly not drawn further than the text requires.

88. MISSALE MOGUNTINUM
    Basle: Wenssler, 1488
    Stillwell M 577
    Weale 625
A:— 4; 6: before and after the Canon.
C:— 1: 1; 2: 10.
D:— 4: a copy in the University Library of Frankfurt-am-Main differs and has A:— 6: before and in the Canon; C:— 1: 1 in, and 2 before the Canon; 2: 10 before, and 7 in the Canon, *Gutenberg-Jahrbuch*, 1935, p. 118.

89. MISSALE MOGUNTINUM
    Mainz: P. Schoeffer, 1493
    Paris BN. Rés. B. 829
    Oxf. Bodl. Douce 280 (2)
    Weale 626
A:— 2 and 3; 6: before and in the Canon.

C:—1: 1; 2: 13; 3: 4; 4: red; 5; 7b.
D:— 4: printer's sign at end; Facs. Molitor, pl. 10.

90. MISSALE MOGUNTINUM
    Speyer: Drach, 1497
    Stillwell M 578
    Weale 627
A:— 3; 6: 11 leaves are inserted before the Canon.
C:— 1: 1; 2: 9; 3: 4, and sometimes 3; 4: red; 5; 7c(?).
D:— 4: richly ornamented Canon 'T', red printer's sign and full colophon in red at the end; the leaves with music not numbered, numbering continues after the leaves with staves.

91. MISSALE MONASTERIENSE
    (MÜNSTER)
    Cologne: Renschen, 1489
    Oxf. Bodl. Auct. VI. Q. infra I. 16
    Weale 641; Voulliéme 808
A: 4; 6: before, in, and after the Canon (fol. 270v).
C:— 1: 2; 2: 10.

92. MISSALE MORINENSE
    (THÉROUANNE)
    Paris: Dupré, 1491
    Stillwell M 579
    not in Weale
A:— 4; 6: in the Canon.
C:— 1: 2; 2: 10.
D:— 4: title, no colophon; year at bottom of fol. 1 b; 2 Canon pictures, on the back of the first one music in MS.; several woodcuts to open the different sections; woodcut borderlines on several of these pages, some in the style of the *livres d'heures*.

93. MISSALE MOZARABICUM
    Toledo: Hagenbach, 1500
    Br.M. C. 17. c. 2
    Paris BN. Rés. B. 268/70
    Paris Ars. f. T. 742, and SG. OE. 15. 166,
    cat. 950
    Stillwell M 623
    Weale 654; Haebler 446
A:— 2; 6: before and in/or after the Canon; the order in this missal making no clear cut between the Canon and the following part.

C:— 1: 1, sometimes 2; 2: 7; 3: 5; 4: red; 5; 7b(c?).

D:— 4: dedication with the woodcut portrait of Fr. Ximenes, Bishop of Toledo; the copy Stillwell M 623 in a binding of Dérome le Jeune.

94. MISSALE NIVERNENSE
Paris: Dupré, 1490
Paris SG. OE. 15. 619, cat. 585
Weale 676
A:— 2; 6: in the Canon.
C:— 1: 2; 2: 9; 3: 4; 4: red; 5; 7c(b?).

95. MISSALE OLOMUCENSE
Nuremberg: Stuchs, 1499
Paris BN. Rés. Vel. 230
Weale 689
A:— 1; 6: fols. 163a–186b, inserted before the Canon.
B:— 2; 3: ♩, otherwise 4; 5: straight; 6: ◦, no stems.
C:— 1: 1; 2: 8; 3: 4; 4: red; 6: a, d(2); 7a, pieces of identical length.
D:— 1: C and F ℰ 𝄷, in the border; 2: ✗; 3: bars separating sentences; 4: the initials of the general text differ from the initials in the part with music.

MISSALE OSCENSE (HUESCA)
Weale 691
See Missale Caesaraugustanum.

96. MISSALE PARISIENSE
Paris: Dupré and Huym, 1481
Oxf. Bodl. Auct. 6. Q. III. 24. 5
Paris BN. Rés. Vél. 914
Paris SG. OE. 15. 228, cat. 343
Weale 699
A:— 2; 6: Prefationes penthecostes.
C:— 1: 2; 2: 10; 3: 4; 4: red; 5; 7b(c?).

97. MISSALE PARISIENSE
Venice: Hamman and Spira, 1487
Paris BN. Rés. B. 4663
Paris Ars. 8° T. 2207
Weale 700
A:— 2 and 3; 6: before and in the Canon.
C:— 1: 2; 2: 9; 3: 4; 4: red; 5; 7c.

98. MISSALE PARISIENSE
Paris: Dupré, 1489
Paris Maz. XV. 560, cat. p. 289
Weale 702

A:— 4; 6: before and in the Canon.
C:— 1: 2; 2: 8, 9, and 10.

99. MISSALE PARISIENSE
Paris: Le Caron and Dupré, 1489
Paris SG. OE. 15. 54, cat. 543
Weale 703
A:— 2; 6: in the Canon.
C:— 1: 2; 2: 8; 3: 4; 4: red; 5; 7c.
D:— 4: ordinary copy of this edition with woodcuts in black and white; Weale and the other bibliographers following him mix this edition up with the following items; Weale gives as printer Bélin who signs as publisher only.

100. MISSALE PARISIENSE
Paris: Le Caron and Dupré, 1489
Paris SG. OE. 15. 579, cat. 543
Weale 703 variant
A:— 2; 6: in the Canon.
C:— 1: 2; 2: 8; 3: 4; 4: red; 5; 7b(c?).
D:— 4: *édition de luxe* of no. 99, on vellum and richly illuminated; the single notes look as if they had been stamped in; the ligatures are written.

101. MISSALE PARISIENSE
Paris: Le Caron and Dupré, 1489
Stillwell M 581
Weale 703 variant
A:— 3; 6: fol. IIIIα and after the Canon which is missing.
C:— 1: 2; 2: 9; 3: 4; 4: red; 5; 7c.

102. MISSALE PARISIENSE
Paris: Higman pro Vostre, 1491
Paris Séminaire de S. Sulpice
Weale 704
A:— 1; 6: before the Canon which is missing.
B:— 1; 3: 𝄞𝄽 ♮; 5: straight, without points; 6: both forms.
C:— 1: 2; 2: 10; 3: 4; 4: red; 5 (added in MS.); 7a.
D:— 1: C and F ℰ 𝄽 𝄴; 2: no guides; 3: black bars separating words.

103. MISSALE PARISIENSE
Paris: Morand, 1496
Paris Ars. f. T. 707
Weale 706
A:— 1; 6: before and in the Canon.

B:— 1; 3: ♭♩ ♯♩ ◘ ♫ ♩; 5: straight, no points; 6: very few stems.

C:— 1: 2; 2: 10; 3: 4; 4: red; 5; 7a.

D:— 1: C and F ♭ ♩ 8; 2: no guides; 3: bars separating words.

104. MISSALE PARISIENSE
Paris: Gering and Rembolt, 1497
Paris BN. Rés. Vél. 177 f
Paris SG. OE. 15. 162 and 685, cat. 873
Paris Maz. 953, cat. p. 514
Stillwell M 582
Weale 708

A:— 1; 6: before, in, and after the Canon.

B:— 1;·3: ♭♩ ♫ ♭; 5: slightly curved, no points; 6: with stems.

C:— 1: 2; 2: 10; 3: 4; 4: red; 5; 7a, pieces of identical length.

D:— 1: C and F ♭ ♩ 8; 2: no guides; 3: bars separating words.

105. MISSALE PATAVIENSE (PASSAU)
Passau: Petri, 1491
Stillwell M 583
Weale 762

A:— 1; 6: 24 leaves inserted before the Canon.

B:— 2; 3: ♩ ◦♩ ♫ mostly 4; 5: ～ not curved, but irregular, with small points; 6: no stems.

C:— 1: 1; 2: 9; 3: 4; 4: red; 5; 7c(?).

D:— 1: C and F ℂ ℭ and ♌; 2: ✓; 3: none; 4: coloured Canon picture and coat of arms.

106. MISSALE PATAVIENSE
Augsburg: Ratdolt, 1494
Paris BN. Rés. Vél. 231
Stillwell M 584
Weale 763

A:— 1; 6: before the Canon, fols. 107–28b.

B:— 2; 3: ♩ ♫ ◦♩ for different intervals; 6: stems to indicate the beginning of a word, the stem reaching over 2 or 3 spaces of the staves.

C:— 1: 1; 2: 9; 3: 4; 4: red; 5; 7a.

D:— 1: C and F ℭ♌; 2: ✓; 3: bars to designate end of antiphon; 4: Canon on vellum; printer's sign in red and black.

107. MISSALE PICTAVIENSE (POITIERS)
Paris: Higman, 1498

Paris SG. OE. 15. 163, cat. 881
Weale 782

A:— 1; 6: before the Canon.

B:— 1; 3: ♭ ♩; mostly 4; 5: slightly curved, no points; 6: no stems.

C:— 1: 2; 2: 10; 3: 4; 4: red; 5; 7a.

D:— 1: C and F ♭ ♩ 8, ♭; 2: none; 3: bars separating words; 4: coloured initials and Canon picture.

MISSALE PRAGENSE
Pilsen: Printer of Statuta Synodalia, 1479.
Stillwell M 585
Weale 795

A:— 5.

108. MISSALE PRAGENSE
Bamberg: Sensenschmidt, 1489
Stillwell M 586
Weale 796

A:— 1; 6: 16 leaves inserted before the Canon, which is added on vellum; in Newberry copy MS. notes on back of Canon picture; the leaves with music and the Canon not numbered, between fol. 148—Canon—and fol. 151.

B:— 2; 3: ♩ ♩ occasionally only; mostly 4; 5: ～ straight, with points; 6: no stems.

C:— 1: 1; 2: 10; 3: 4; 4: red; 6: a, d(2); 7c.

D:— 1: C and F ℭ ℬ or ♀; 2: ◊ in border; 3: bars separating sentences; 4: collation differs from Weale.

109. MISSALE PRAGENSE
Leipzig: Kachelofen, 1498
Br. M. IC. 12348
Paris BN. Rés. B. 1495
Weale 798; Lib. 28

A:— 1; 6: before the Canon.

B:— 2; 3: ♩, mostly 4; 5: straight, no points; 6: no stems.

C:— 1: 1; 2: 8; 3: 4; 4: red; 6: a, d(2); 7b.

D:— 1: C ♌; 2: ✓; 3: bars separating sentences.

ORDO MISSAE RATISPONENSIS
Br. M. IA. 1747
See Ordinarium Ratisponense.

110. MISSALE RATISPONENSE
Bamberg: Sensenschmidt, 1485
Oxf. Bodl. Auct. 4. Q. II. 4
Weale 806

A:— 1; 6: before the Canon.

B:— 2; 3: ♫, mostly 4; 5: straight, no points; 6: stems occasionally only.

C:— 1: 1; 2: 10; 3: 4; 4: red; 6: d(2); 7c.

D:— 1: C and F 𝄡 ♭, ♭; 2: ◊; 3: bars separating sentences; 4: Facs. Molitor, pl. 6.

III. MISSALE RATISPONENSE
Bamberg: Petzensteiner and Pfeyl, 1492
Oxf. Bodl. Q. sub fen. I. 17
Stillwell M 588
Weale 807

A:— 1; 6: before the Canon.

B:— 2; the setting of the music is almost identical with that of the previous item, Weale 806; the rubrics and the initials are different. In the edition of 1485 on fols. 6b and 14a of the part with music a word is added with notes in print in the margin at the bottom, the space not having been figured out correctly; this is corrected in this edition.

112. MISSALE RATISPONENSE
Bamberg: Petzensteiner, Sensenschmidt and Pfeyl, 1492
Oxf. Bodl. Auct. 4. Q. II. 6
Weale 808

A:— 1.

D:— 4: the part with music almost identical with the preceding number.

113. MISSALE RATISPONENSE
Bamberg: Pfeyl, 1497
Stillwell M 589
Weale 810

A:— 1; 6: 17 leaves inserted before the Canon.

B:— 2; 3: ♫, mostly 4; 5: straight, no points; 6: stem to indicate beginning of word.

C:— 1: 1; 2: 10; 3: 4; 4: red; 6: a, d(2); 7a.

D:— 1: C and F 𝄡 ♭; 2: ✓ in border; 3: bars separating sentences; 4: Canon missing; Facs. Molitor, pl. 17.

114. MISSALE RATISPONENSE
Bamberg: Pfeyl, 1500
Oxf. Bodl. Auct. IV. Q. II. 6
Stillwell M 590
Weale 811

A:— 1; 6: before the Canon, 16 fols. and one short quotation on fol. CLXVIII; numbering starts again after the Canon with CC.

B:— 2; 3: ♫ ♫; mostly 4; 5: straight, no points; 6: stems occasionally only.

C:— 1: 1; 2: 10; 3: 4; 4: red; 6: d(2); 7a.

D:— 1: C and F 𝄡 ♭; 2: ✓; 3: bars separating sentences.

115. MISSALE REDONENSE (RENNES)
Poitiers: Bouyer and Bellesculé, *c.* 1491
Paris BN. Rés. B. 28988
Weale 817

A:— 4; 6: before and in the Canon.

C:— 1: 2; 2: 7.

D:— 4: for colophon see A. Claudin, *Documents sur la typographie*, ii. 429.

116. MISSALE REDONENSE
Paris: Hodian and Alexander, 1492
Paris BN. Rés. Vél. 201
Weale 818

A:— 1; 6: before, in, and after the Canon.

B:— 1; 3: ♫ ♫ ♫ and the usual ligatures; 5: straight; 6: no stems.

C:— 1: 2; 2: 10; 3: 4; 4: red; 5; 7a.

D:— 1: C and F ♫ ♫ 8; 2: none; 3: bars separating words; 4: very exact setting, with beautiful small initials similar to Missale Leodiense, no. 85.

MISSALE REDONENSE
Rouen: Mauditier and Olivier, 1500
Paris BN. Rés. B. 27922
Weale 819

A:— 5.

117. MISSALE ROMANUM
Lyons: Claudius Giboletus, 14 . .
Paris SG. OE. 15. 620 (not in cat.)
Weale 843

A:— 4; 6: before the Canon of which part is missing.

C:— 1: 2; 2: 9.

D:— 4: printer's sign at end.

118. MISSALE ROMANUM
Milan: Zarotus, 1476, April 26
Paris BN. Rés. B. 866
Weale 854

A:— 4; 6: before and in the Canon.

C:— 1: 2; 2: 7 and 8.

D:— 4: staves drawn very regularly with

raster, musical notes throughout in MS.; on folio directly before the Canon, music and text in MS.

119. MISSALE ROMANUM
Rome: Han, 1476, Oct. 12
Paris BN. Rés. B. 865
Stillwell M 591
Weale 855
A:— 1; 6: before and in the Canon.
B:— 1; 3: ♭ ♮; 5: straight; 6: with stems.
C:— 1: 2; 2: 10; 3: 5; 4: red; 5; 7b.
D:— 1: C [; 2: ✓; 3: bars separating sentences; 4: Paris copy on large paper; Facs. Molitor, pl. 1.

120. MISSALE ROMANUM
Venice: Siliprandis, 1477
Br.M. IB. 20702
Paris BN. Rés. 867
Weale 856; Lib. 29
A:— 4; 6: before and in the Canon, which is set in the regular type, not in special Canon type.
C:— 1: 1; 2: 8.
D:— 4: occasional lines with roman notes in MS.; in the Paris copy on leaf k i b: A:— 3; C:— 3: 4; 4: red; 7c.

121. MISSALE ROMANUM
Naples: Moravus, 1477
Paris BN. Rés. Vél. 132
Weale 857
A:— 3, in the Canon partly 4; 6: before and in the Canon.
C:— 1: 2; 2: 9; 3: 4; 4: red; 5; 7b.
D:— 4: Facs. Riemann, pl. 12, taken from a copy where staves are drawn with a raster.

122. MISSALE ROMANUM
Venice: s. typ., 1479
Paris BN. Rés. B. 869
Weale 859
A:— 4; 6: before and after the Canon.
C:— 1: 2; 2: 8.
D:— 4: space for Canon picture left free.

123. MISSALE ROMANUM
Milan: Zarotus, 1479
Paris BN. Rés. B. 61
Weale 860
A:— 4; 6: before and in the Canon.

C:— 1: 2; 2: 8.
D:— 4: space for initials left free.

124. MISSALE ROMANUM
Milan: Pachel and Scinzenzeler, 1480
Br.M. IA. 26454
Weale 864; Lib. 30
A:— 4; 6: before and in the Canon.
C:— 1: 1; 2: 9.

125. MISSALE ROMANUM
Venice: Oct. Scotus, 1481
Paris BN. Rés. B. 1633 f
Paris Maz. 292, cat. p. 156
Weale 870
A:— 2, and 3 on last leaf verso of Canon; 6: before and in the Canon.
C:— 1: 2; 2: 6; 3: 4; 4: red; 5; 7b(c?).
D:— 4: small 4°.

126. MISSALE ROMANUM
Venice: Oct. Scotus, 1481 quarto kal.
  Januarij
Stillwell M 593
Weale 870 variant
A:— 4; 6: before and in the Canon.
C:— 1: 2; 2: 6.
D:— 4: staves with three lines are drawn apparently with a raster; partly musical notes in MS.; only on fol. r ij b one row printed stave with four lines, metal ledges.

MISSALE ROMANUM
Venice: Renner, 1481
Br.M. IA. 19880
Paris BN. Rés. B. 11520
Paris Maz. 297, cat. p. 159
Stillwell M 592
Weale 871; Lib. 31
A:— 5.
D:— 4: in the British Museum copy 5 leaves have been added before and 3 leaves after the Canon. These contain notes, text, initials, border, and lines in MS. Three of the lines are red, but the two outer lines are black. The MS. is all very regular—almost as regular as print.

127. MISSALE ROMANUM
Venice: Oct. Scotus, 1482
Br.M. IA. 21185
Oxf. Bodl. Auct. 1. Q. VII. 12
Stillwell M 594
Weale 877; Lib. 32

A:— 1; 6: before and in the Canon.

B:— 1; 3: the usual ligatures to denote ascent or descent between two notes; for the most part 4; 5: straight; 6: with stems.

C:— 1: 2; 2: 8; 3: 4; 4: red; 5; 7c.

D:— 1: C and F ♭ ♮♭; 2: ✓; 3: occasionally bars separating words.

128. MISSALE ROMANUM
Albi: Numeister, *c.* 1483
Paris Maz. 1192, cat. p. 658
Weale 881

A:— 3; and in the Canon sometimes 2; 6: before and in the Canon.

C:— 1: 2; 2: 8 before and 11 in the Canon; 3: 4; 4: red; 5; 7b.

D:— 4: in the Canon the staves are arranged in two columns against the text running over the whole line; no Canon picture.

129. MISSALE ROMANUM
Venice: Benalius, Arrivabene and Paganinis, 1483
Stillwell M 596
Weale 884

A:— 1; 6: before the Canon.

B:— 1; 3: ♭ ♮ (often in this way, not connected) ♪♭ ♮ ♮%, for the most part 4; 5: ♮ curved, no points; 6: with stems.

C:— 1: 2; 2: 8; 3: 4; 4: red; 5; 7c.

D:— 1: C and F ♭ ♮♭; 2: ✓; 3: bars separating sentences; 4: there are two styles in the setting of the music, the three last columns of it, two of them on the verso of the Canon picture, have no guides and numerous ligatures; small 4°.

MISSALE ROMANUM (SLAV.)
Venice: Torresanus, 1483
Stillwell M 595
Weale 1330

A:— 5.

130. MISSALE ROMANUM
Naples: Preller? or Gontier?, *c.* 1488
Cambridge, Mass., Harvard Lib.
Weale 887

A:— 1; 6: before and in the Canon.

B:— 1; 3: ♭ ♮ ♮♭, for the most part 4; 5: straight; 6: no stems.

C:— 1: 2; 2: 9; 3: 4; 4: red; 5; 7b(?).

D:— 1: F ♮♭; 2: ♭; 3: bars between sentences, and sometimes before the last word; 4: small coloured Canon picture.

131. MISSALE ROMANUM
Venice: Benalius, 1484
Paris BN. Rés. Vél. 133
Weale 888

A:— 1; 6: before and in the Canon.

B:— 1; 3: ♭ and the usual ligatures, for the most part 4; 5: curved ♮ with points; 6: with stems.

C:— 1: 2; 2: 10; 3: 4; 4: red; 5; 7c.

D:— 1: C and F ♭ ♮♭; 2: ✓; 3: bars separating sentences; 4: the notes, rather small, hang in the spaces between the lines.

132. MISSALE ROMANUM
Venice: Arrivabene and Paganinis, 1484
Br.M. IB. 22487
Weale 889; Lib. 34

A:— 1; 6: before and in the Canon.

B:— 1; 3: ♭ ♮ ♭; 5: curved, no points; 6: both forms.

C:— 1: 2; 2: 11; 3: 4; 4: red; 5; 7c.

D:— 1: C and F ♭ ♮♭; 2: ✓; 3: bars separating words.

MISSALE ROMANUM
Nuremberg: Stuchs, 1484
Br.M.C. 9. a. 4
Cambridge UL., Oates 1088
Paris BN. Rés. B. 2674
Stillwell M 597
Weale 890

A:— 5.

D:— 4: *Katalog der Musik-Bibliothek Paul Hirsch*, iii, no. 66.

133. MISSALE ROMANUM
Venice: Girardengus, 1484
Paris BN. Rés. B. 1635
Weale 891

A:— 1, 2, and 3; 6: before and in the Canon.

B:— 1; 3: the usual ligatures, for different sizes and intervals; 5: straight; 6: long stems.

C:— 1: 2; 2: 8; 3: 4; 4: red; 5; 7a, three pieces for each row.

D:— 1: C and F ♭ ♮ 8 ;2: ✓; 3: bars separating sentences.

134. MISSALE ROMANUM
Pavia: Girardengus, 1484
Paris BN. Rés. B. 62
Weale 891a
A:— 1 in the part directly before the Canon,
otherwise 3; 6: before and in the Canon.
B:— 1; 3: the usual ligatures; 5: straight;
6: with stems.
C:— 1: 2; 2: 8; 3: 4; 4: red; 5; 7a.
D:— 1: F ⑨ 8; 2: ✓; 3: bars separating sen-
tences.

135. MISSALE ROMANUM
Lyons: Hus, 1485
Br.M. IB. 41701
Paris BN. Rés. B. 871
Weale 894
A:— 2 and 3; 6: before and in the Canon.
C:— 1: 2; 2: 8; 3: 4; 4: red; 5; 7c.

MISSALE ROMANUM
Venice: Petrus de Plasiis, 1485
Stillwell M 598
Weale 895
A:— 5.
D:— 4: editor is Philippus de Rotingo Man-
tuanus. Stillwell gives erroneously Palta-
sichis as printer, mixing up Weale 895 and
896.

136. MISSALE ROMANUM
Venice: Paltasichis, 1485
Br.M. IA. 21903
Weale 896; Lib. 34
A:— 3; 6: before and in the Canon.
C:— 1: 1; 2: 9; 3: 4; 4: red; 5; 7c.

137. MISSALE ROMANUM
Venice: Francfordia, 1487
Br.M. IA. 22043
Stillwell M 599
Weale 900; Lib. 35
A:— 3; 6: before and in the Canon.
C:— 1: 2; 2: 8; 3: 4; 4: red; 5; 7c.

138. MISSALE ROMANUM
Milan: Zarotus, 1488
Paris BN. Rés. B. 874
Weale 902
A:— 1; 6: before and in the Canon.
B:— 1; 3: ⅃ ⚹ for the most part 4; 5: straight;
6: with stems.
C:—1: 2; 2: 8; 3: 4; 4: red; 5; 7b(c?).

D:— 1: C and F ⌊ ⅃⌊; 2: ♩; 3: bars separating sentences.

139. MISSALE ROMANUM
Venice: Hamman, 1488
Paris BN. Rés. B. 872 and Vél. 134
Weale 904
A:— 1; 6: before and in the Canon.
B:— 1; 3: ⌐♭⅃ ⌐, for the final notes ↝;
5: curved, sometimes points; 6: with stems.
C:— 1: 2; 2: 8; 3: 4; 4: red; 5; 7b(?).
D:— 1: C and F ⌜ ⅃⌜; 2: ✓; 3: bars
separating words; 4: Facs. Molitor, pl. 41.

140. MISSALE ROMANUM
Rome: Planck, 1488
Paris BN. Rés. Vél. 1466
Weale 905
A:— 1; 6: before and in the Canon.
B:— 1; 3: ⚹⚹ and the usual; 5: straight; 6:
with stems.
C:— 1: 2; 2: 5; 3: 5; 4: red; 5; 7b(c?).
D:— 1: C ⌊; 2: ✓; 3: bars separating sen-
tences.

141. MISSALE ROMANUM
Venice: de Tortis, 1489
Br.M. IA. 21400
Stillwell M 600
Weale 907; Lib. 36
A:— 1; 6: before and in the Canon.
B:— 1, 3 ⅃; for the most part 4; 5: curved ⅂
with points; 6: with stems for the most part.
C:— 1: 2; 2: 8; 3: 4; 4: red; 5; 7c.
D:— 1: C and F ⌊ ⅃⌊; 2: ✓; 3: occasionally,
very irregular black bars separating words.

142. MISSALE ROMANUM
Venice: s. typ., c. 1490
Br.M. IA. 25100
Cambridge UL., Oates 2228
Weale 912; Lib. 37
A:— 1; 6: before and in the Canon.
B:— 1; 3: ⅃ ⌐; for the most part 4; 5: slightly
curved; 6: with stems.
C:— 1: 2; 2: 9; 3: 4; 4: red; 5; 7c.
D:— 1: F ⅃ ⌊; 2: ᴗ; 3: bars separating sen-
tences; 4: in both copies colophon without
printer's name; following Weale 'Giunta',
following *BMC.* v. 591 'unassigned type,
similar to Tortis'.

143. MISSALE ROMANUM
Venice: Sessa, 1490
Oxf. Bodl. Don. f. 137
Paris SG. OE. 15. 620, cat. 601
Weale 914
A:— 4; 6: before and in the Canon.
C:— 1: 2; 2: 8.
D:— 4: with printer's sign; Canon picture missing.

144. MISSALE ROMANUM
Venice: Novimagio, 1491
Paris BN. Rés. B. 2677
Weale 915
A:— 1; 6: before and in the Canon.
B:— 1; 3: ⏑ and the usual, for the most part 4; 5: curved; 6: with stems.
C:— 1: 2; 2: 8; 3: 4; 4: red; 5: 7c.
D:— 1: C and F ⬡ ⬡; 2: ✓; 3: occasionally bars separating sentences.

145. MISSALE ROMANUM
Pavia: Girardengus and Birreta, 1491
Br.M. IA. 31415
Weale 916; Lib. 38
A:— 3; 6: before and in the Canon.
C:— 1: 2; 2: 9; 3: 4; 4: red; 5: 7c.

146. MISSALE ROMANUM
Nuremberg: Fratres ord. Eremiti, 1491
Cambridge UL., Oates 1076
Weale 918
A:— 1; 6: before (only one short quotation) and in the Canon.
B:— 1; 3: ⬡ ⬡, for the greater part 4; 5: straight, no points; 6: no stems.
C:— 1: 1 and 2; 2: 10 (?, no complete page occurring in the book); 3: 4; 4: red; 6: d (2 at the front, and one occasionally at the end); 7a.
D:— 1: C and F ⬡ ⬡; 2: none; 3: none; 4: coloured Canon picture.

147. MISSALE ROMANUM
Milan: Zarotus, 1492
Stillwell M 602
Weale 920
A:— 1 and 3 in the last staves before the Canon: 6: before and in the Canon which is set in two columns.
B:— 1; 3: ⬡ ⬡ ⬡, and some long fioriture

without text in 4; 5: straight, without points; 6: with stems, but also ♦.
C:— 1: 2; 2: 8; 3: 4; 4: red; 5: 7b.
D:— 1: C and F ⬡ ⬡; 2: ⬡; 3: bars between sentences, occasionally.

148. MISSALE ROMANUM
s. loc.: s. typ., 1492
Oxf. Bodl. Auct. 1. Q. VI. 67
Stillwell M 603
Weale 921
A:— 4, in the copy of the Library of Congress in some places (fol. p8) possibly 3; 6: before and in the Canon.
C:— 1: 2; 2: 6, 8 and 9; 3: 3 and 4; 4: red; 5; 7c(?).
D:— 4: initials MS.; Proctor 7423 'French', but probably German.

149. MISSALE ROMANUM
Brescia: Jac. et Ang. de Britannicis, 1492
Paris BN. Rés. B. 63
Weale 922
A:— 1; 6: before and in the Canon.
B:— 1; 3: ⬡; 5: with points; 6: with long stems.
C:— 1: 2; 2: 9; 3: 4; 4: red; 5; 7b.
D:— 1: C and F ⬡ ⬡; 2: ✓; 3: bars separating sentences.

150. MISSALE ROMANUM
Venice: Spira, 1493
Br.M. IA. 24206
Stillwell M 604
Weale 924; Lib. 39
A:— 1; 6: before and in the Canon.
B:— 1; 3: ⬡ ⬡ ⬡ ⬡ and the usual forms to denote ascent and descent of two notes; 5: curved, without points; 6: with stems.
C:— 1: 2; 2: 8; 3: 4; 4: black; 5; 7c?
D:— 1: C and F ⬡ ⬡; 2: ✓; 3: no bars; 4: printed from woodblock; the lines of the staves and the clefs very irregular; the form of the notes similar to Spira's type; Facs. Molitor, pl. 14.

151. MISSALE ROMANUM
Venice: Hamman, 1493 Kal. Jul.
Br.M. IA. 23359
Cambridge UL., Oates 2036
Paris BN. Rés. B. 27739

Stillwell M 605
Weale 925; Lib. 40
A:— 1; 6: before and in the Canon.
B:— 1; 3: rich in ligatures ♩ ♭ ♩ ♩ ⌐;
5: ♩; 6: with stems.
C:— 1: 2; 2: 7; 3: 4; 4: red; 5; 7b.
D:— 1: F ♩ ͡ ; 2: ✓; 3: bars between words.

152. MISSALE ROMANUM
Venice: Hamman, 1493 Kal. Dec.
Br.M. IA. 23364
Stillwell M 606
Weale 926; Lib. 41
A:— 1; 6: before and in the Canon.
B:— 1; 3: rich in ligatures ♩ ♩ ♩ ♩, at
the end ⌐; 5: ○ ♩; 6: with stems.
C:— 1: 2; 2: 7; 3: 4; 4: red; 5; 7c.
D:— 1: F ♩ ͡ ; 2: ⌣; 3: bars between words;
4: Facs. Molitor, pl. 15.

153. MISSALE ROMANUM
Venice: Spira, 1494
Paris BN. Rés. B. 2678
Weale 929
A:— 1; 6: before and in the Canon.
B:— 1; 3: ⌐ and the usual ligatures; 5:
straight; 6: with stems.
C:— 1: 2; 2: 6; 3: 4; 4: red; 5; 7c(?).
D:— 1: C and F ͡ ○⅛; 2: ✓; 3: bars between
sentences.

154. MISSALE ROMANUM
Venice: Pincius, 1495
Stillwell M 607
Weale 931
A:— 1; 6: before and in the Canon.
B:— 1; 3: ♭ ♩ ⌐, for the greater part 4;
on last pages more ligatures; 5: ♩ slightly
curved, some points; 6: with stems.
C:— 1: 2; 2: 6; 3: 5; 4: red; 5; 7b(c?).
D:— 1: C and F ͡ ♩ ͡ ; 2: ⌒ or ⌣ not
throughout; 3: bars between sentences,
not throughout.

MISSALE ROMANUM
Lisbon: Moravus, 1496
Br.M. IA. 56660
not in Weale
A:— 5.
D:— 4: Explicit votivale missarum secundum

ritum romane curie; 8°; fol. B4 Tabula
missarum; beautiful red initials; printer's
sign at end.

155. MISSALE ROMANUM
Rome: Planck, 1496
Br.M. IB. 18578
Weale 934; Lib. 42
A:— 1; 6: before and in the Canon.
B:— 1; 3: ♭ ♩ ♭ ♩%; 5: straight; 6: with
stems.
C:— 1: 2; 2: 7; 3: 5; 4: red; 5; 7b.
D:— 1: C ͡ ; 2: ✓; 3: bars between words.

156. MISSALE ROMANUM
Venice: Hamman, 1497
Stillwell M 608
Weale 938
A:— 1; 6: before and in the Canon.
B:— 1; 3: ♭ ♩, for the greater part 4; 5: ♩
slightly curved, small points; 6: with stems.
C:— 1: 2; 2: 6 (in the Canon also); 3: 4;
4: red; 5; 6: b(occasionally), d(1); 7a.
D:— 1: F ♩ ͡ ; 2: ✓; 3: bars between sen-
tences; 4: some staves are left without text
or music.

157. MISSALE ROMANUM
Venice: Sessa, 1497
Paris BN. Rés. B. 2673
Weale 939
A:— 1; 6: before and in the Canon.
B:— 1; 3: ⌐ ⌐ and the usual ligatures,
often intermixed with ◊; 5: ♩; 6: with
stems.
C:— 1: 2; 2: 8; 3: 4; 4: red; 5; 7a, pieces of
identical length.
D:— 1: C and F ͡ ♩ ͡ ; 2: ✓; 3: bars between
sentences.

158. MISSALE ROMANUM
Venice: Spira, 1497
Br.M. IA. 24229
Weale 941; Lib. 43
A:— 1; 6: before and in the Canon.
B:— 1; 3: the usual ligatures for ascent and
descent, but rare; 5: straight; 6: with stems.
C:— 1: 2; 2: 6; 3: 4; 4: red; 5; 7a.
D:— 1: C and F ͡ ○⅛; 2: ✓; 3: bars between
words.

159. MISSALE ROMANUM
  Venice: Bevilaqua, 1497
  Paris BN. Rés. B. 3823
  Weale 942
A:— 1; 6: before and in the Canon.
B:— 1; 3: ⌐ ⌐ and the usual ligatures;
  5: small points; 6: with stems.
C:— 1: 2; 2: 7; 3: 4; 4: red; 5; 7b, space for
  initials of text left free.
D:— 1: F ♮°; 2: ✓; 3: bars between sen-
  tences.

160. MISSALE ROMANUM
  Venice: Sessa, not after 1498 (1490?)
  Br.M. IA. 24573
  Weale 943; Lib. 44
A:— 1; 6: from 'Die palmarum' to 'Sabbatho
  sancto ord. missae'.
B:— 1; 3: ⌐ ⌐ ⌐, at the end ⌐, for the
  most part resolved; 5: straight; 6: with
  stems.
C:— 1: 2; 2: 7; 3: 4; 4: red; 5; 7c.
D:— 1: C and F ⌐ ♮⌐; 2: ✓; 3: bars between
  words.

161. MISSALE ROMANUM
  Venice: Sessa, not after 1498 (1490?)
  Stillwell M 601
  Weale 943 variant
A:— 1; 6: before and in the Canon.
B:— 1: 3: ⌐ ⌐ ⌐, at the end ⌐, for the
  greater part resolved 4; 5: slightly curved,
  small points; 6: with stems.
C:— 1: 2; 2: 7; 3: 4; 4: red; 5; 7b.
D:— 1: C and F ⌐ (small), ♮⌐ ⌐⌐; 2: ✓;
  3: bars between sentences; 4: this edition is
  different from the previous item, as well as
  from Weale 914.

162. MISSALE ROMANUM
  Venice: Spira, 1498 4 kal. Jul.
  Paris SG. OE. 15. 482, cat. 886
  Weale 945
A:— 1; 6: before and in the Canon.
B:— 1; 3: ⌐⌐ ⌐ ⌐; 5: slightly curved,
  with small points in the ligatures; 6: with
  stems.
C:— 1: 2; 2: 10; 3: 4; 4: red; 5; 7a.
D:— 1: C and F ⌐ ♮⌐; 2: ✓; 3: bars between
  sentences.

163. MISSALE ROMANUM
  Venice: Spira, 1498 id. Oct.
  Br.M. IA. 24234
  Paris BN. Rés. B. 11521
  Stillwell M 609
  Weale 946; Lib. 45
A:— 1; 6: before the Canon.
B:— 1; 3: ⌐⌐⌐ and the usual forms; 5:
  slightly curved, with small points; 6: with
  stems.
C:— 1: 2; 2: 7; 3: 4; 4: red; 5; 7b.
D:— 1: C and F ⌐ ♮⌐; 2: ✓; 3: bars between
  sentences; 4: edit. Petrus Arrivabene; 8°.

164. MISSALE ROMANUM
  Milan: Pachel, 1499
  New York Metropolitan Museum
  Weale 949
A:— 1; 6: before the Canon.
B:— 1; 3: ⌐⌐% ⌐ for the greater part 4;
  5: curved, with points; 6: with stems.
C:— 1: 2; 2: 11; 3: 4; 4: red; 5; 7a.
D:— 1: C ⌐; 2: ✓; 3: bars between sen-
  tences; 4: only copy on record, three wood-
  cuts representing St. Peter, Crucifixion, and
  Annunciation; colophon missing.

165. MISSALE ROMANUM
  Venice: Arrivabene, 1499
  Paris BN. Rés. Vél. 135
  Weale 950
A:— 1; 6: before and in the Canon.
B:— 1; 3: ⌐ ⌐% ⌐ and the usual forms;
  5: ♮, but not throughout with points; 6:
  with stems.
C:— 1: 2; 2: 9; 3: 4; 4: red; 5; 7a.
D:— 1: C and F ⌐ ♮⌐; 2: ✓; 3: bars between
  sentences; 4: *édition de luxe* on large paper.

166. MISSALE ROMANUM
  Lyons: Maréchal and Chaussard, 1499
  Oxf. Bodl. Inc. f. F. 2 $\frac{1499}{1}$
  Weale 951
A:— 1; 6: before and in the Canon.
B:— 1; 3: ⌐⌐ ⌐ ⌐ ⌐% ⌐; 5: slightly curved,
  no points; 6: both forms.
C:— 1: 2; 2: 6; 3: 4; 4: red; 5; 7b.
D:— 1: C and F ⌐ ♮⌐; 2: ✓, only occasion-
  ally; 3: bars between sentences; 4: small 4°.

167. MISSALE ROMANUM
Venice: Pincius, *c.* 1500
Stillwell M 610
Weale 953
A:— 4; 6: before and in the Canon.
C:— 1: 2; 2: 9; 5.
D:— 4: coloured Canon picture and initials.

168. MISSALE ROMANUM
s. loc.: s. typ., *c.* 1500
Paris BN. Rés. Vél. 136
Weale 954
A:— 4; 6: before the Canon, which in this copy is MS.
C:— 1: 2; 2: 10; 5.
D:— 4: probably earlier than 1500.

169. MISSALE ROMANUM
Lyons: Sachon, 1500
Paris BN. Rés. B. 27725
Weale 955
A:— 1; 6: before and in the Canon.
B:— 1; 4; 5: curved ◠; 6: with stems for the finalis only.
C:— 1: 2; 2: 8; 3: 4; 4: red; 5; 7a.
D:— 1: C ℂ; 2: ✓; 3: bars occasionally to separate notes of the same pitch.

170. MISSALE ROMANUM
Lyons: Sachon, 1500
Br.M. IB. 42179
Paris BN. Rés. B. 64
Weale 956
A:— 1; 6: before and in the Canon.
B:— 1; 3: ⌐, otherwise 4; 5: ◠ curved, no points; 6: stems to indicate end of sentence.
C:— 1: 2; 2: 8; 3: 4; 4: red; 5; 7a.
D:— 1: C ℂ; 2: ✓ occasionally only; 3: bars occasionally; 4: almost identical with previous item.

171. MISSALE ROTHOMAGENSE (ROUEN)
Rouen: Morin, 1495
Paris SG. OE. 15. 664, cat. 781
Weale 1343
A:— 2; 6: before and in the Canon.
C:— 1: 2; 2: 14; 3: 4; 4: red; 5; 7b.
D:— 4: richly ornamented initials and Canon picture.

172. MISSALE ROTHOMAGENSE
Rouen: Morin, 1499

Br.M. IC. 43975
Weale 1344
A:— 3; 6: before and in the Canon.
C:— 1: 2; 2: 13; 3: 4; 4: red; 5; 7b(c?).

173. MISSALE SAGIENSE (SÉEZ)
Rouen: Le Talleur, 1488
Paris BN. Rés. B. 927 (2nd version)
Paris Ars. Th. 2752 (1st and 2nd versions)
Weale 1371
A:— 2; 6: before and in the Canon.
C:— 1: 2; 2: 13; 3: 4; 4: red; 5; 7c.
D:— 4: Lit.: P. Le Verdier, *L'Atelier de Guillaume le Talleur*, 1916, with a facsimile of the page with the MS. musical notes.

MISSALE SAGIENSE
Rouen: Morin, 1496
Paris BN. Rés. B. 1475 (II)
Weale 1372
A:— (5)
D:— 4: one leaf, m1 only; woodcut border, small 4°; the complete copy at Caen not accessible for examination.

174. MISSALE SAGIENSE
Rouen: Regnault, 1500
Paris SG. OE. 15. 486, cat. 968
Weale 1373
A:— 1; 6: before and in the Canon.
B:— 1; 3: ♭♮ for different intervals; 5: straight; 6: no stems.
C:— 1: 2; 2: 11; 3: 4; 4: red; 5; 7a.
D:— 1: C and F ⌐ ⌐ 8; 2: none; 3: bars between sentences.

175. MISSALE SALTZBURGENSE
Nuremberg: Stuchs, 1492
Stillwell M 611
Weale 1378
A:— 1; 6: fols. CLXIXa–CLXXXIIb, inserted before the Canon.
B:— 2; 3: ⌐ ⌐ ⌐, for the greater part 4; 5: irregular, no points; 6: no stems.
C:— 1: 1; 2: 9; 3: 4; 4: red; 6: a, d(2); 7b, possibly border together with staves printed from woodblock.
D:— 1: C and F ⌐ 𝔅; 2: ✓ in borderlines; 3: bars between sentences; 4: Facs. Riemann, pl. 21.

176. MISSALE SALTZBURGENSE
Nuremberg: Stuchs and Ryman, 1498

Stillwell M 612
Weale 1379
A:— 1; 6: before the Canon two closed gatherings are inserted, fols. ʟxxɪɪɪɪa–ʟxxvɪɪɪb and cxʟɪa–cʟɪvb.
B:— 2; 3: ⅋ ⌂ for different intervals; for the greater part 4; 6: no stems.
C:— 1: 1; 2: 8; 3: 4; 4: red; 6: a, d(2); 7b, possibly the staves together with the border printed from woodblock.
D:— 1: C and F ᶜ ♭; 2: ✓ in borderline; 3: bars between sentences.

177. MISSALE SARUM
Basle: Wenssler, *c.* 1489
Br.M. IC. 37140
Oxf. Bodl. Gough Missal 33
Weale 1388
A:— 1, in some parts 4; 6: before and in the Canon.
B:— 1; 3: ⌐ ♭; 5: straight, with points; 6: both forms.
C:— 1: 1; 2: 9; 3: 4; 4: red; 6: a, d(2); 7c.
D:— 1: C and F ᶜ ℞; 2: ᗡ; 3: no bars; 4: neither Wenssler nor Kilchen is mentioned in the colophon. The type of the text is Wenssler's, with the exception of a set of small black initials, as on fols. 84b, 87a, and 97a and b. Lit.: K. Stehlin, 'Regesten', in *Archiv für Geschichte des deutschen Buchhandels*, vols. xi–xiv, xx; there two documents are listed referring to negotiations of Wenssler with England; see also Scholderer in *The Library*, 3rd Ser., vi, July 1912.

178. MISSALE SARUM
Rouen: Morin, 1492
Br.M. IB. 43955
Weale 1389
A:— 3; 6: before and after the Canon.
C:— 1: 2; 2: 13; 3: 4; 4: red; 5; 7c.
D:— 4: printer's sign at the end; coloured Canon picture and illuminated 'T'; on some leaves woodcut border.

179. MISSALE SARUM
Venice: Hamman, 1494
Cambridge UL., Oates 2041–2
Oxf. Bodl. Douce b. 1 (28/29) frg.
Weale 1390
A:— 1; 6: before, in, and after the Canon.

B:— 1; 3: ♩ ♩ ♭ ♭; 5: straight, small points, sometimes ◇; 6: with stems.
C:— 1: 2, and 1 in the Canon; 2: 9; 3: 4; 4: red; 5; 7a.
D:— 1: C ℭ; 2: ✓; 3: occasionally bars between sentences; folio; in the Bodleian two leaves without music.

180. MISSALE SARUM
Venice: Hamman, 1494
Br.M. IA. 23373
Weale 1391; Lib. 46
A:— 1; 6: before and in the Canon.
B:— 1; 3: ℕ and at the end ↷, otherwise the usual ligatures; 5: slightly curved, with small points; 6: with stems.
C:— 1 in, and 2 before the Canon; 2: 7; 3: 4; 4: red; 5; 7c.
D:— 1: C and F ᶜ ⅋♭; 2: ✓; 3: occasionally bars between sentences; 4: small 4°.

181. MISSALE SARUM
Rouen: Morin, 1497
Cambridge, St. Catharine's College
Weale 1392
A:— 1; 6: before, in, and after the Canon.
B:— 1; 3: ⅊♭ ♭ ⅋ ⅋ρ; 5: straight, no points; 6: three forms ⅂ or ◦ or ◖.
C:— 1: 2; 2: 10; 3: 4; 4: red; 5; 7a.
D:— 1: C and F ᶜ ⅂ 8; 2: none; 3: bars between sentences; 4: Canon on vellum, several woodcuts.

182. MISSALE SARUM
Rouen: Morin, 1497
Br.M. IC. 43955
Stillwell M 614
Weale 1393
A:— 1; 6: before, in, and after the Canon.
B:— 1; 3: ℕ⌐ ⌐ and the usual forms, sometimes 4; 5: straight, without points; 6: stems to indicate the end of a word.
C:— 1: 2; 2: 11; 3: 4; 4: red; 5; 7a.
D:— C ℭ; 2: ♪; 3: bars between sentences; 4: *édition de luxe*; Lit.: Hind, vol. ii, p. 626.

183. MISSALE SARUM
Paris: Gering, 1497
Stillwell M 613
Weale 1394
A:— 1; 6: before and in the Canon.

B:— 1; 3: ♭ ♩♩, the latter form for different intervals, for the greater part 4; 5: straight, no points; 6: stems only occasionally, for the greater part ◊.
C:— 1: 2; 2: 9 and 10; 3: 4; 4: red; 5; 7a.
D:— 1: C and F ♭ ♮ 8; 2: ♪; 3: bars between sentences; 4: several woodcuts beside the Canon picture; initials MS. in red and blue.

184. MISSALE SARUM
Westminster: Notary and Barbier, 1498
Br.M. IB. 55292
Cambridge UL., Oates 4157
Weale 1395
A:— 3; 6: before and in the Canon.
C:— 1: 2; 2: 9; 3: 4; 4: red; 5; 7b.

185. MISSALE SARUM
Paris: Higman, 1500
Oxf. Bodl. Gough Missal 26
Weale 1396
A:— 1; 6: before and after the Canon, the Canon in the copy in MS.
B:— 1; 3: ♮ ♭, for the greater part 4; 5: ◠ slightly curved, no points; 6: stems to denote beginning and end of a word; after the Canon, fol. B11 for the single note ◒.
C:— 1: 2; 2: 10; 3: 4; 4: red; 5; 7a.
D:— 1: C ♭; 2: none; 3: bars between words.

186. MISSALE SARUM
London: Pynson, 1500
Oxf. Bodl. Auct. I. Q. infra I. 56
Cambridge UL. frg., Oates 4201
Weale 1398
A:— 1; 6: before, in, and after the Canon.
B:— 1; 3: ♭ ♩ ♯♩ ♩ ♩ ♩ ♫ ; 5: slightly curved in the part before the Canon ◠, after ◊; 6: no stems, only in the part after the Canon to denote the end of a word.
C:— 1: 2; 2: 10; 3: 4; 4: red; 5; 7a.
D:— 1: C and F ♭ ♮ 8 and b ♮; 2: ♪; 3: bars between sentences; 4: title on fol. 11 following calendarium; woodcut with coat of arms between calendarium and text.

MISSALE SLESWICENSE
Schleswig: Arndes, c. 1475
Cambridge UL., Oates 1323
Weale 1466
A:— 5.

D:— 4: Officia sacerdotis in celebratione Missae; 16 leaves, Incipit 'Cum sacerdos exuit vestes suas'; Finis 'Missa finita dic inclinando'; fol. 11 'Te igitur'; contains the chief prayers of the priest during Mass, but differs from a regular missal in not giving the antiphons, &c.; folio; Weale gives the date 1486.

MISSALE SPECIALE
Augsburg: Ratdolt, c. 1490
Stillwell M 625
Weale 1472
A:— 5.
D:— 4: the title reads 'Missae speciales'; this edition is listed by Schottenloher after the *Missale speciale Augustense,* 1505; Weale mixes up both editions, in giving the title of our copy and dating it c. 1504.

MISSALE SPECIALE
Strasbourg: Grüninger, 1493
Paris BN. Rés. B. 1456
Weale 1468
A:— 5.
D:— 4: title: Speciale opus missarum de officiis dominicalibus per anni circulum de summis festivitatibus . . . una cum commune sanctorum; Lit.: Haebler, 'Joh. Grüninger der Drucker des Missale mit dem Kanon Peter Schoeffers', in *Beiträge zur Inkunabelkunde,* N.F., iv, 1911.

MISSALE SPECIALE
Strasbourg: Grüninger, c. 1498
Br.M. 52. g. 7
Weale 1469
A:— 5.
D:— 4: in the index on fol. 2, 'misse speciales' include: 'de angelis, de caritate, pro pace, tempore synodi, pro iter agente, contra pestilentiam, Missa Maximiliani regis contra turcos', referring to the victory at Villach in 1492; thus the MS. entry in the copy 'c. 1480' cannot be right; in the Br. M. catalogue the year is given as 1503; Weale gives c. 1498, which might be right; Lit.: Haebler, as in annotation of preceding item.

MISSALE SPECIALE
Strasbourg: Pruess, c. 1500
Stillwell M 624
Weale 1471
A:— 5.

D:— 4: combination of a general and special missal.

187. MISSALE SPIRENSE
Bamberg: Sensenschmidt and Petzensteiner, 1487
Oxf. Bodl. Auct. VI. Q. I. 8
Paris BN. Rés. Vél. 234
Weale 1482
A:— 1; 6: 22 leaves with music are inserted, before the Canon, between fols. 170 and 171.
B:— 2; 3: ℣; for the greater part 4; 5: with points; 6: both forms alternating.
C:— 1: 1; 2: 10; 3: 4; 4: red; 6: a, d(2); 7b(c?).
D:— 1: C and F ℭ Ⅎ; 2: ↗; 3: bars between sentences.

188. MISSALE STRENGNENSE (STRÄNGNÄS)
Lübeck: Ghotan, 1487
Cambridge UL., Oates 1185
Oxf. Bodl. frg. 258875 c. 1
Paris BN. Rés. Vél. 802 frg.
Stillwell M 615 frg.
Weale 1486
A:— 2; 6: all copies manc.
C:— 1: 2; 2: 12; 3: 4; 4: red; 5; 7b.
D:— 4: only the fragments in the Pierpont Morgan Library (5 leaves) and in the Bibliothèque Nationale (2 leaves) have staves; the leaf in the Klemming copy at the Bibliothèque Nationale has no music.

189. MISSALE STRIGONENSE (GRAN)
Venice: Spira, 1498
Stillwell M 616
Weale 1498
A:— 2; 6: before and in the Canon.
C:— 1: 2; 2: 9; 3: 4; 4: red; 5; 7a.
D:— 4: Canon picture and printer's sign at the end.

190. MISSALE STRIGONENSE
Venice: Paep, 1500
Stillwell M 617
Weale 1499
A:— 3; 6: before and in the Canon.
C:— 1: 2; 2: 6 and 7; 3: 4; 4: red; 5; 7a.
D:— 4: date in colophon 'Anno dni. mccccc ij kal. Aprilis'; Stillwell is doubtful whether the date is Mar. 30, 1500 or April 1st, 1502.

191. MISSALE TARENTASIE (TARANTAISE)
s. loc.: s. typ., s.a.
Paris BN. Rés. B. 1484
Weale 1525
A:— 1; 6: before and in the Canon.
B:— 1; 3: ♩, for the greater part 4; 5: straight; 6: stems occasionally to denote beginning of a word.
C:— 1: 2; 2: 8; 3: 4; 4: red; 6: c, d(2 at top, otherwise one line); 7b.
D:— 1, C and F ℭ Ⅎℭ; 2: none; 3: bars between sentences.

192. MISSALE TARRACONENSE
Tarragona?: Rosenbach, 1499
Stillwell M 618 (not in the Lib. of Congress, but in the Hispanic Soc., New York)
Weale 1527; Haebler 448
A:— 3; 6: before, in, and after the Canon.
C:— 1: 2; 2: 8; 3: 4; 4: red; 5; 6: on some pages elaborate woodcut borders surrounding the whole page; 7b.
D:— 4: two Canon pictures; printer's sign at end.

193. MISSALE TORNACENSE (TOURNAI)
Paris: Higman, 1498
Paris BN. Rés. B. 1489
Stillwell M 619
Weale 1546
A:— 1; 6: before and in the Canon.
B:— 1; 3: ♭♮ for small intervals, otherwise 4; 5: slightly curved ◠, no points; 6: no stems.
C:— 1: 2; 2: 10; 3: 4; 4: red; 5; 7a.
D:— 1: C and F ℭ Ⅎℭ; 2: none; 3: bars between words; 4: Canon 'T' in MS.; some woodcuts in the style of the *livres d'heures*.

194. MISSALE TRAJECTENSE (UTRECHT)
Paris: Higman and Hopyl, 1497
Br.M. IB. 40145 manc.
Paris BN. Rés. Vél. 784
Paris SG. OE. 15. 480, cat. 866
Paris Maz. 949, cat. p. 512
Stillwell M 620
Weale 1554
A:— 1; 6: before and in the Canon.

B:— 2; 3: 𝄐, for the greater part 4; 5: straight, with points ↘ ; 6: 𝄐 .

C:— 1: 2; 2: 10; 3: 4; 4: red; 5; 7a.

D:— 1: C and F ⌒ one beneath the other; 2: ✓; 3: bars between words.

195. MISSALE TRECENSE (TROYES)
s. loc.: s. typ., s.a.
Paris SG. OE. 15. 721, cat. 1042
Weale 1560

A:— 2; 6: before and in the Canon.

C:— 1: 2; 2: 10; 3: 4; 4: red; 5; 7b.

D:— 4: the musical notes written very carefully; Canon picture on vellum.

196. MISSALE TRECENSE
Paris: Dupré, 1500
Paris BN. Rés. Vél. 922
Weale 1563

A:— 2; 6: before and in the Canon.

C:— 1: 2; 2: 10; 3: 4; 4: red; 5; 7b or in MS. with raster.

D:— 4: the lines of the staves follow the creases in the vellum.

197. MISSALE TREVERENSE (TRIER)
Basle: Wenssler, *c.* 1488
Br.M. IB. 37138
Paris BN. Rés. Vél. 149 (frg. of Canon only)
Weale 1575; Lib. 47

A:— 2 and 3; 6: before and in the Canon.

C:— 1: 1; 2: 10; 3: 4; 4: red; 6: a, d (2 lines in the British Museum copy, one in the Paris copy); 7c(?).

198. MISSALE TULLENSE (TOUL)
Paris: Le Rouge, 1493
Paris BN. Rés. Vél. 816
Weale 1584

A:— 2; 6: before the Canon.

C:— 1: 2; 2: 7; 3: 4; 4: red; 5; 7a.

199. MISSALE TURONENSE (TOURS)
Rouen: Morin, 1493
Paris BN. Rés. B. 1481
Paris SG. OE. 15. 264, cat. 658
Weale 1595

A:— 2; 6: before and in the Canon.

C:— 1: 2; 2: 13; 3: 4; 4: red; 5; 7b.

D:— 4: *édition de luxe* on vellum with coloured borders and ornaments in the text; no Canon picture.

200. MISSALE TURONENSE
s. loc.: s. typ., 1500
Paris BN. Rés. Vél. 920
Weale 1596

A:— 2; 6: before—Praefationes—and in the Canon.

C:— 1: 2; 2: 11; 3: 3; 4: red; 5; 7b.

201. MISSALE UCETIENSE (UZÈS)
Lyons: Numeister and Topié, 1495
Br.M. IB. 41819
Weale 1605

A:— 1; 6: Supplement of 31 fols. at the end, incipit 'Nato canunt omnia', explicit 'dona eis requiem. Amen'.

B:— 1; 3: ♭ and the usual forms; 5: straight, with points; 6: stems to denote end of sentence.

C:— 1: 1; 2: 10; 3: 4; 4: red; 5; 7b.

D:— 1: C and F ♮ ⸠; 2: ✓ ; 3: red bars between sentences; 4: facsimile, M. Audin in *Le Bibliophile*, Paris, 1931–2.

202. MISSALE UPSALENSE
s. loc.: s. typ., before 1487
Paris BN. Rés. Vél. 801
Cambridge UL. and Oxf. Bodl. one leaf each in Klemming's Sveriges äldre liturgiska literatur
Weale 1609

A:— 3; 6: before, in, and after the Canon.

C:— 1: 2; 2: 8; 3: 4; 4: red; 7b (c?).

D:— 4: no staves on the leaves in Cambridge and Oxford.

203. MISSALE VIRDUNENSE (VERDUN)
Paris: Dupré, 1481
Paris BN. Rés. B. 942
Weale 1636

A:— 4; 6: before and in the Canon.

C:— 1: 2; 2: 10.

MISSALE VRATISLAVIENSE
Mainz: Schoeffer, 1483
Stillwell M 622
Weale 1653

A:— 5.

D:— 4: coloured Canon picture and 'T'.

204. MISSALE VRATISLAVIENSE
Strasbourg: Pruess, *c.* 1487
Stillwell M 558
Weale 1655? H. 11265

A:— 4; 6: before the Canon.

C:— 1: 2; 2: 8 and 10.

D:— 4: initials in MS.; the last leaf is added in facsimile with a wrong colophon: 'Missale Basiliense' by Kesler in Basle; Stillwell lists the book as Weale 157; but this is a Missale Vratislaviense; on fol. 303a a 'chorus Wratislaviense scti Stanislai' is mentioned, and in the calendar a festival 'Wenceslai'; Elephant folio.

MISSALE VRATISLAVIENSE
Mainz: Schoeffer, 1499
Br.M. IC. 266
Weale 1658

A:— 5.

205. MISSALE WORMATIENSE
Basle: Wenssler, c. 1488
Br.M. IC. 37141
Weale 1649

A:— 1; 6: before the Canon, from fol. 124 on —a^8 b^8 c^{10}.

B:— 2; 3: ♩ ♫ for different intervals; 5: slightly curved, with points; 6: both forms ◇ and 9.

C:— 1: 1; 2: 8; 3: 4; 4: red; 6: a, d(2); 7c (b?).

D:— 1: C and F ♫ ♪ ♭; 2: ✓; 3: bars between sentences; 4: ends with Sequentiale; colophon missing; the calendarium printed with another type, M 29, used otherwise by some Bamberg printers; the copy in the library at Darmstadt, Germany, seems to belong to the same edition, and differs only in so far as it has music also in the Canon, and that A:— 3; listed by Weale as 1650. *Gutenberg-Jahrbuch*, 1935, no. 18.

MISSALE XANTONENSE (SAINTES)
Paris: s. typ., 1490
Br.M. IA. 41362
Weale 1662

A:— 5.

206. MISSALE XANTONENSE
Paris: Higman, 1491
Cambridge UL., Oates 3026
Weale 1663

A:— 1; 6: before and in the Canon.

B:— 1; 3: ♭ ♮; 5: ⌐ curved, no points; 6: no stems.

C:— 1: 2; 2: 10; 3: 4; 4: red; 5; 7a.

D:— 1: C and F ♭ ♮8 ; 2: none; 3: bars between words; 4: coloured Canon picture; copy on vellum.

MISSALE ORD. S. BENEDICTI BURSFELDENSE
Eltville: Fratres communes, c. 1475
Weale 1679
Identical with Ceremoniale Bursfeldense, Marienthal, *Br.M. IA. 9706*.

207. MISSALE BENEDICTINUM
Bamberg: Sensenschmidt, 1481
Br.M. IB. 2617
Oxf. Bodl. Auct. 6 Q. I. 9
Paris BN. Rés. Vél. 245 and Vél. 778 frg.
Weale 1680; Lib. 49

A:— 3 and 4; 6: before and in the Canon.

C:— 1: 1; 2: 9; 3: 5; 4: black; 6: a, d(1); 7b(?).

D:— 4: in the British Museum and in the Oxford copy staves and notes written very carefully, the form of the notes resembling Wenssler's type; red division strokes; handwriting in the Paris copy very careless, Facs. Riemann, pl. 13.

208. MISSALE BENEDICTINUM BURSFELDENSE
Speyer: Drach, 1498
Br.M. IB. 8657
Stillwell M 541
Weale 1681 and 1681 (A); Lib. 48

A:— 2; in the British Museum copy 3, with notes written very carefully; 6: before the Canon.

C:— 1: 1; 2: 8; 3: 4; 4: red; 5; 7c.

D:— 4: in the Kyriale the lines of the staves go so far only as the text requires, see introduction; numbering goes on after the Canon with fol. cxlv; in the British Museum copy one row is added in black in MS. on fol. cxliiib; division strokes in MS.

MISSALE BENEDICTINUM MELLICENSE
Nuremberg: Stuchs, c. 1499
Br.M. IB. 8120
Stillwell M 542
Weale 1703; Lib. 50

A:— 5.

MISSALE CARTHUSIENSE
Speyer: Drach, c. 1498
Br.M. IB. 8660
Oxf. Bodl. Auct. 6 Q. I. 21
Paris BN. Rés. Vél. 256
Weale 1728; Lib. 51
A:— 5.
D:— 4: Canon picture; in Oxford dated
c. 1490.

MISSALE CISTERCIENSE
Strasbourg: Grueninger, 1487
Br.M. IB. 1388
Oxf. Bodl. Auct. 6 Q. 3. 20
Paris BN. Rés. B. 1491
Weale 1751; Lib. 52
A:— 5.

MISSALE CLUNIACENSE
Cluny: Wenssler, 1493
Paris BN. Rés. Vél. 811 frg. and B. 308
Weale 1792
A:— 5.

209. MISSALE ORD. HUMILIATORUM
Milan: Zarotus, 1490
Paris BN. Rés. Vél. 260
Weale 1800
A:— 2; 6: before and in the Canon.
C:— 1: 2; 2: 9; 3: 4; 4: red; 5; 7b.
D:— 4: musical notes very carefully written,
resembling type; ink much faded.

210. MISSALE ORD. EREMITARUM
S. PAULI
Augsburg: Ratdolt, c. 1495
Cambridge UL.
Weale 1811
A:— 2 and 3; 6: before and in the Canon.
C:— 1: 2 before and 1 in the Canon; 2: 10;
5; 7b.
D:— 4: imprint given in Oates as: Brünn,
Stahel and Preunlein.

211. MISSALE ORD. PRAEDICATORUM
Milan: Zarotus, 1482
Stillwell M 545
not in Weale
A:— 4; 6: before and in the Canon.
C:— 1: 2; 2: 8; 5.

212. MISSALE ORD. PRAEDICATORUM
Venice: Oct. Scotus, 1482
Br.M. IA. 21186

Oxf. Bodl. Auct. I. Q. VII. 12
Stillwell M 544
Weale 1815; Lib. 53
A:— 1; 6: before and in the Canon.
B:— 1; 3: ♭ ♮, sometimes resolved ¶♭;
5: straight, no points; 6: with stems.
C:— 1: 2; 2: 8; 3: 4; 4: red; 5; 7c.
D:— 1: C and F ℭ ¶ℭ; 2: ⁄; 3: bars between
sentences; 4: on the back of the leaf before
the Canon 6 staves with the text only 'Ite
missa est' and no musical notes; Facs. Rie-
mann, pl. 14.

213. MISSALE ORD. PRAEDICATORUM
Naples: Moravus, 1483
Br.M. IB. 29423
Paris BN. Rés. Vél. 1704
Weale 1816; Lib. 54
A:— 2; 6: before the Canon.
C:— 1: 2; 2: 8; 3: 4; 4: red; 5; 7c.

214. MISSALE ORD. PRAEDICATORUM
Venice: Francfordia, 1484
Br.M. IA. 22033
Paris BN. Rés. B. 11515
Weale 1817; Lib. 55
A:— 2, and 2 and 3 in the British Museum
copy; 6: before and in the Canon.
C:— 1: 2; 2: 8; 3: 4; 4: red; 5; 7c.

215. MISSALE ORD. PRAEDICATORUM
Venice: Hamman, 1494
Br.M. IA. 23366
Paris BN. Rés. B. 11516
Weale 1822; Lib. 56
A:— 1; 6: before and in the Canon.
B:— 1; 3: the usual; 5: ♮; 6: with stems.
C:— 1: 2; 2: 7; 3: 4; 4: red; 5; 7c(?).
D:— 1: F ¶ℭ; 2: ⁄; 3: bars between words.

216. MISSALE ORD. PRAEDICATORUM
Venice: Torresanus, 1496
Br.M. IB. 21741
Paris BN. Rés. Vél. 263
Oxf. Bodl. Auct. VI. Q. I. 20
Weale 1823; Lib. 57
A:— 1; 6: before and in the Canon.
B:— 1; 3: ♭ ♮ ♯; 5: straight; 6: with stems.
C:— 1: 2; 2: 9; 3: 4; 4: red; 5; 7b.
D:— 1: C and F ℭ ¶ℭ; 2: ⁄; 3: bars
between words.

217. MISSALE ORD. PRAEDICATORUM
Venice: Bevilaqua, 1497
Paris BN. Rés. B. 11517
Weale 1824
A:— 1; 6: before and in the Canon.
B:— 1; 3: ♭ ♩ ♫ ♪ ♩; 5: small points; 6: with stems.
C:— 1: 2; 2: 7; 3: 4, sometimes 3, thus on fol. 73b; 4: red; 5; 7c.
D:— 1: F ♩ ⌐; 2: ✓; 3: bars between sentences.

218. MISSALE ORD. PRAEDICATORUM
Venice: Spira, 1500
Oxf. Bodl. Douce B. B. 85
Paris Maz. XV. 1083, cat. p. 596
Weale 1825
A:— 1; 6: before and after the Canon.
B:— 1; 3: ♫ ♩ ♭ ♪, and for a great part 4; 5: curved; 6: with stems.
C:— 1: 2; 2: 7; 3: 4; 4: red; 5; 7b(?).
D:— 1: F ♩⌐; 2: ✓; 3: bars between sentences.

219. MISSALE CARMELITORUM
Brescia: de Boninis, 1490
Paris BN. Rés. Vél. 262
Weale 1884
A:— 1; 6: before and in the Canon.
B:— 1; 3: ♩ ♫; 5: small points; 6: with stems.
C:— 1: 2; 2: 9; 3: 4; 4: red; 5; 7c.
D:— 1: C and F ⌐♩⌐; 2: ✓; 3: bars between sentences.

220. MISSALE CARMELITORUM
Venice: Giunta, 1500
Paris Maz. XV. 1078 A, cat. p. 594
Weale 1885
A:— 1; 6: before and in the Canon.
B:— 1; 3: ♭ ♩ ♫ ♩°° ♫ ♩; 5: curved, with points; 6: with stems.
C:— 1: 2; 2: 10; 3: 4; 4: red; 5; 7b(a?).
D:— 1: C and F ℂ ♩ℂ; 2: ✓; 3: bars between sentences.

221. MISSALE FRATRUM MINORUM
s. loc.: s. typ., s.a.
Stillwell M 551
Weale 1913

A:— 2; 6: before and in the Canon; perhaps also after the Canon, where space is left free before the Benedictio panis.
C:— 1: 2; 2: 7; 3: 3; 4: red; 5; 7b.

MISSALE DOMINORUM
TEUTONICORUM
Nuremberg: Stuchs, 1499
Br.M. IC. 8117
Oxf. Bodl. Douce 273
Weale 1936; Lib. 58
A:— 5.

222. OBSEQUIALE AUGUSTENSE
Augsburg: Ratdolt, 1487
Br.M. IA. 6652
Paris BN. Rés. B. 2978 and Vél. 1674
Stillwell O 1
Boh. 742; 743; Lib. 59
A:— 1; 6: throughout, beginning with Commemoratio dominice resurrectionis.
B:— 2; 3: ♫ ♫ ♩ ◦♩; 5: curved, with points; 6: both forms.
C:— 1: 1; 2: 5; 3: 4; 4: red; 5; 7b(c?).
D:— 1: C and F ℂ ℂ and ♩ ♩; 2: no guides; 3: bars between sentences; 4: almost identical editions; they differ in the form of the clefs and in the colophon; BN. B. 2978, Br.M. IA. 6652, and Stillwell have the date Cal. Februarii and the explicit in red; Vél. 1674 has the date Cal. Julii and the explicit in black. Hain and Bohatta list two editions, but with the same date. If the editions have to be separated
B. 2978 = Stillwell O 1 = Hain 11925 = Boh. 743.
Vél. 1674 = Hain 11926 = Boh. 742; Facs. Molitor, pl. 7.

223. OBSEQUIALE AUGUSTENSE
Augsburg: Ratdolt, 1489
Paris BN. Rés. B. 2943, not in Boh.; not in Schottenloher
A:— 1; 6: throughout, beginning with the Commemoratio dominice resurrectionis.
B:— 2; 3: ♩ ♫; 6: with stems in ligatures only, ◦♩.
C:— 1: 1; 2: 5; 3: 4; 4: red; 5; 7a, pieces of identical length.
D:— 1: C and F ℂ ℂ; 2: ✓; 3: bars between sentences.

224. OBSEQUIALE AUGUSTENSE
Augsburg: Ratdolt, 1499
Br.M. IA. 6780

Oxf. Bodl. Inc. e. G. 5, $\frac{1499}{1}$

Stillwell O 2
Boh. 744; Lib. 60
A:— 1; 6: throughout.
B:— 2; 3: ♩ ♩ ♫; 6: stems in loose ligatures only.
C:— 1: 1; 2: 5; 3: 4; 4: red; 5; 7a.
D:— 1: C and F ℭ ℱ; 2: ℰ; 3: bars between sentences.

OBSEQUIALE BRIXINENSE,
see Ceremoniale Brixinense.

225. OBSEQUIALE EYSTETENSE
Eichstädt: Reyser, 1488
Paris BN. Rés. B. 948
Boh. 748
A:— 1; 6: throughout.
B:— 2; 3: ♫ ♩ for different intervals; but for the greater part 4; 6: with stems for the lunga.
C:— 1: 1; 2: 7; 3: 4; 4: red; 6: a, d(1); 7c.
D:— 1: C and F ℯ ℱ; 2: ✓; 3: occasionally bars at end of musical motive.

OBSEQUIALE FRISINGENSE
Bamberg: Sensenschmidt and Petzensteiner, 1484
Oxf. Bodl. Auct. I. Q. VII. 45
Cambridge UL., Oates 275
Boh. 749
A:— 5.
D:— 4: the book is called Obsequiale seu benedictionale on the title, and Libellus obsequialium at the end.

OBSEQUIALE FRISINGENSE
Augsburg: Ratdolt, 1493
Br.M. IA. 6736
Boh. 750; Lib. 61
A:— 5.

226. OBSEQUIALE RATISPONENSE
Nuremberg: Stuchs, 1491
Br.M. IA. 8071
Oxf. Bodl. Auct. I. Q. VII. 44
Paris BN. Rés. Vél. 2901

Stillwell O 4
Boh. 751; Lib. 62
A:— 1; 6: throughout.
B:— 2; 3: ♫ ♩ for different intervals; for a great part 4; 5: straight, without points; 6: stems for centre note of a melodic motive.
C:— 1: 1; 2: 6; 3: 4; 4: red; 6: a, d(2); 7a.
D:— 1: C and F ℰ ℬ; 2: ✓; 3: bars between sentences; 4: woodcut by Michael Wohlgemuth.

227. OBSEQUIALE SALTZBURGENSE
Nuremberg: Stuchs, 1496
Stillwell O 5
Boh. 752
A:— 1 and 3; 6: throughout.
B:— 2; 3: ♫ ♩ o♪; on some pages 4 only; 5: straight, no points; 6: both forms, for liquescens ♪.
C:— 1: 1; 2: 7; 3: 4; 4: red; 6: a, d(2); 7a, with lines printed first, then the notes.
D:— 1: C ℰ in border; 2: ♭ and ♂ in border; 3: bars between sentences, occasionally red single or double bars at beginning and end of stave.

The following Officia are listed to show the variety of their content:
Offices of the Holy Virgin
Offices of Saints
Offices of other festivals
General offices

OFFICIUM B. MARIE VIRGINIS
Valencia: de la Roca, 1486
Br.M. IA. 52034
Stillwell O 34
Haebler 491
A:— 5.
D:— 4: explicit officium beate marie virginis . . . de toto anno ad longum sine remissionibus cum missa eiusdem et septem psalmis penitentialibus et officium defunctorum, etc.

OFFICIA B. MARIE VIRGINIS
Coria: de Lila (?), before 1489
Oxf. Bodl. Inc. b. S. 97. 5
Haebler 492
A:— 5.
D:— 4: contains the antiphons, hymns, &c., from several offices for the Holy Virgin.

OFFICIUM B. MARIE VIRGINIS
Venice: Hamman, 1491
Paris BN. Rés. Vél. 1470
Bohatta, Bibliographie der Livres d'heures,
1924, p. 65
A:— 5.
D:— 4: contains the penitential psalms and the funeral offices.

OFFICIUM S. HOMOBONI CRE-
MONAE
Cremona: Darlerius, *c.* 1495
Cambridge UL., Oates 2608
A:— 5.
D:— 4: woodcut of the saint on the title; contains the antiphons, &c., of the office without the historia.

OFFICIUM S. LEOPOLDI
Passau: Petri, s.a.
Br.M. IA. 11342
A:— 5.
D:— 4: the closing song of this office, the historia, printed with melodies, see no. 21.

OFFICIUM S. LEOPOLDI
Vienna: Cassis, s.a.
Br.M. IA. 51509
A:— 5.

OFFICIUM DE VISITATIONE
Westminster: Caxton, s.a.
Br.M. IA. 55065
A:— 5.
D:— 4: part of the office of the Holy Virgin.

OFFICIUM DE TRANSFIGURA-
TIONE JESU CHRISTI
London: Pynson, s.a.
Br.M. IA. 55557
A:— 5.
D:— 4: contains the offices celebrated during the month of August.

OFFICIUM
Naples: Moravus, 1487
Stillwell O 35
A:— 5.
D:— 4: contains Calendar, officium B.M.V., psalmi penitentiales, officium mortuorum, officium s. crucis, officium s. spiritus, orationes.

OFFICIUM
Venice: Hamman, 1493
Br.M. IA. 23362
Stillwell O 40
A:— 5.
D:— 4: Incipit 'Domine labia mea aperies'; contains psalmi penitentiales, officium s. crucis, officium s. spiritus, officium mortuorum; the book is written for a monastery and has liturgical rubrics for the fratres and sorores.

OFFICIUM MISSAE
Magdeburg: Alb. Ravenstein and Joach. Westphal, 1483
Stillwell O 49
A:— 5.
D:— 4: explains the rubrics and lists the corresponding liturgical duties.

OFFICIUM QUOTIDIANUM
Ferrara: Magister Laurentius de Rubeis, 1497
Br.M. IA. 25755
Stillwell O 45
A:— 5.
D:— 4: Calendarium; preface explaining the short form of this book; service of the hours, listing the antiphons, the psalms, the hymns, the orations, emphasizing the offices of the saints; perhaps published for use in a convent.

OFFICIUM QUOTIDIANUM
Zaragossa: Hurus, 1499
Stillwell O 27
Haebler 489
A:— 5.
D:— 4: Calendarium, Speculum Conscientiae (that is catechism of the decalogue), service of the hours, Litanie; among the offices: officium s. spiritus, officium sancti angeli custod., officium corporis Christi die Jovis dicendum, officia mortuorum; the beginnings of the antiphons, &c., are accompanied by notes on the liturgical duties of the priest.

ORDINARIUM ARGENTINENSE
Strasbourg: Pruess, 1477
Paris Maz. XV. 101, cat. p. 164
Boh. 754
A:— 5.
D:— 4: title: Regule indicantes ordinem cujuslibet diei.

ORDINARIUM BENEDICTINUM BURSFELDENSE
Marienthal: Fratres Communes, 1474/5
Br.M. IA. 9712
Stillwell O 77
Boh. 756
A:— 5.

ORDINARIUM CISTERCIENSE
Paris: Pigouchet, *c.* 1497
Oxf. Bodl. Douce 29
not in Boh.
A:— 5.
D.— 4: subtitle on fol. a viiib 'Officium b. M. v. secundum usum ordinis Cisterciensis'; the book has the form of a book of hours.

ORDINARIUM COLONIENSE
Cologne: Koelhof, the elder, 1486
Br.M. IA. 3590
Stillwell O 78
Boh. 762; Voulliéme 870; Lib. 63
A:— 5.

ORDINARIUM LEODIENSE
Cologne: Renschen, 1492
Br.M. IA. 4465
Paris BN. Rés. B. 2916
Paris Maz. XV. 648, cat. p. 336
Boh. 767; Voulliéme 873
A:— 5.
D.— 4: woodcut on title.

ORDINARIUM OFFICII (RITUALE)
Milan: s. typ., *c.* 1477/80
Oxf. Bodl. Auct. VI. Q. VI. 39
Boh. 1047
A:— 5.
D.— 4: Incipit ordo officii ad faciendum aquam benedictam; called Rituale Ambrosianum on binding, by Proctor and by Bohatta.

228a. ORDINARIUM PRAEMONSTRATENSE
Lübeck: Matth. Brandis, *c.* 1485
Br. M. IB. 9935
Stillwell O 79 (a)
Boh. 770 (769?); Lib. 64
A:— 4; 6: on fols. 43a–47b, in the chapters following the 'De dedicatione ecclesiae'.
C:— 1: 1; 2: lines are left free as required by text.

D:— 4: this edition has 50 ll. and starts with a calendar, followed by an index of the chapters; the copy in the Morgan Library, New York, is bound together with the following edition.

228b. ORDINARIUM PRAEMONSTRATENSE
Lübeck: Matth. Brandis, 1485
Stillwell O 79(b)
Boh. 771
A:— 4; 6: on fols. 49a–53a, in the chapters 'de festis sanctorum' and 'de officiis mortuorum'.
C:— 1: 1; 2: lines are left free as required by text.
D:— 4: this edition has 54 ll., and does not start with a calendar; attributed by Collijn to Koch, Magdeburg.

ORDINARIUM PRAEMONSTRATENSE
s. loc.: s. typ., *c.* 1500
Br.M. IA. 1412
Boh. 768
A:— 5.
D:— 4: Incipit ordinarium partis estivalis scm ordinem Premonstratensem; first leaf with ornamented border.

ORDINARIUM RATISPONENSE
Strasbourg: Pruess, s.a.
Br.M. IA. 1747
not in Weale, not in Boh.
A:— 5.
D:— 4: title 'Ordo misse Ratisponensis'.

The following Ordinaria are listed by Bohatta partly as Ordinaria and partly as Directoria, and in the British Museum catalogue as Ceremonialia.

ORDINARIUM SARUM
Westminster: Caxton, 1478(?)
Br.M. C. 40. 11 (5)
Boh. 772
A:— 5.
D:— 4: title 'Ordinale seu Pica secundum usum Sarum'; ed. Clement Maydeston; modern reprint in the Henry Bradshaw Society Publications, vol. vii, 1894.

ORDINARIUM SARUM
Westminster: Caxton, 1487
Br.M. C. 10. b. 16
Boh. 773
A:— 5.

ORDINARIUM SARUM
Antwerp: Leeu, 1488
see Directorium Sarum

ORDINARIUM SARUM
Westminster: de Worde, 1495
see Directorium Sarum

ORDINARIUM SARUM
London: Pynson, 1497
see Directorium Sarum

ORDINARIUM TURONENSE
Paris: Levet, 1500
Paris Maz. XV. 1093, cat. p. 602
Boh. 776
A:— 5.
D: 4: Bohatta 'Parisiis, *c.* 1500'.

229. PONTIFICALE
Rome: Planck, 1485
Paris BN. Rés. B. 92/94
Paris SG. OE. 15. 153, cat. 457
Stillwell P 852
Boh. 777
A:— 1; 6: throughout.
B:— 1; 3: ♭ ♮ ; 5: straight, sometimes ◆;
6: with stems.
C:— 1: 2; 2: 7; 3: 5; 4: red; 5; 7c.
D:— 1: C ; 2: ✗; occasionally bars
between sentences.

230. PONTIFICALE
Rome: Planck, 1497
Br.M. IB. 18581
Paris BN. Rés. B. 95/96
Paris SG. OE. 15. 479, cat. 856
Stillwell P 853
Boh. 778; Lib. 65
A:— 1; 6: throughout, beginning from fol.
51b.
B:— 1; 3: ♭ ♮◇ for different intervals; 5:
straight; 6: with stems.
C:— 1: 2; 2: 8; 3: 5; 4: red; 5; 7b.
D:— 1: C ; 2: ✗; 3: occasionally bars
between sentences; 4: see Introduction,
p. xxxii.

231. PROCESSIONALE ORD. S. BENE-
DICTI DE VALLADOLID
Montserrat: Luschner, 1500
Br.M. IA. 54315
Stillwell P 914
Boh. 779; Haebler 556
A:— 1; 6: throughout.
B:— 1; 3: ♮ ♮ ♮ ♮◇; for a great part
4; 5: slightly curved, without points; 6: no
stems.
C:— 1: 1; 2: 5; 3: 4; 4: red; 5; 7a.
D:— 1: C and F ♭ ; 2: ♩; 3: bars between
words; 4: richly ornamented initials, wood-
cut on the title.

232. PROCESSIONARIUM ROMANUM
ET FRATRUM MINORUM
Rouen: Olivier pro Regnault, s.a.
Paris BN. Rés. B. 27759
not in Boh.
A:— 1; 6: throughout.
B:— 1; 3: ♮ ♮ ♮ ♩♩ ♮, for differ-
ent intervals; 5: straight; 6: no stems.
C:— 1: 1; 2: 5; 3: 4; 4: red; 5; 7a, pieces of
identical length.
D:— 1: C and F ♭ ; 2: ♩, occasionally;
3: bars between sentences; 4: colophon
'Impensis Regnault'; the name of Olivier
taken from the file index.

233. PROCESSIONARIUM ORD. PRAE-
DICATORUM
Seville: Ungut and Polonus, 1494
Br.M. IA. 52382
Paris BN. Rés. B. 27936
Boh. 781; Haebler 557
A:— 1; 6: throughout.
B:— 1; 3: ♮ ♮ ♩ and the usual forms, for
different intervals; 5: with points; 6: no
stems.
C:— 1: 1; 2: 6; 3: 4; 4: red; 5; 7c(b?).
D:— 1: C and F ♭ ♩♭; 2: ✗; 3: red bars
between words; 4: space left free for
initials; facs., Audin, in *Le Bibliophile*, Paris,
1931–2.

234. PROCESSIONARIUM ORD. PRAE-
DICATORUM
Venice: Spira, 1493
Paris BN. Rés. B. 27379 and 27720
not in Boh.

A:— 1; 6: throughout.

B:— 1; 3: ⵎ ⵎ and the usual forms; 5: straight, no points; 6: with stems.

C:— 1: 1; 2: 5; 3: 4; 4: red; 5; 7c.

C:— 1: C and F 𝄴 ⵎ; 2: ✓; 3: bars between sentences.

235. PROCESSIONARIUM ORD. PRAE-
DICATORUM
Venice: Spira, 1494
Br. M. IA. 24214
Stillwell P 913
Boh. 782; Lib. 66

A:— 1; 6: throughout.

B:— 1; 3: rich in ligatures, the usual forms and ⵎ ⵎ ⵎ ⵎ ⵎ ⵎ ⵎ ⵎ; 5: straight, no points; 6: with stems.

C:— 1: 1; 2: 5; 3: 4; 4: red; 5; 7b.

D:— 1: C and F 𝄴 ⵎ; 2: ✓; 3: bars between sentences; 4: frontispiece woodcut with representation of procession, several small woodcuts with the representation of the sacramental services.

The psalters are arranged in the alphabetical order of the places of printing (those with no place of printing being given first); then, in the alphabetical order of the printers, and then in chronological order; the number in Bohatta's Bibliography has been added where possible.

PSALTERIUM
s.l.: s. typ., s.a.
Paris BN. Rés. Vél. 1460
Boh. 801?

A:— 5.

PSALTERIUM
s.l.: s. typ., s.a.
Paris BN. Rés. B. 16377

A:— 5.

D:— 4: 196 leaves; explicit Hymnarius, ends with index, small 8°.

PSALTERIUM
German?: s. typ., s.a.
Cambridge UL.

A:— 5.

D:— 4: 139 num. fols. 4°; some musical notes added later in MS.

PSALTERIUM
Paris?: s. typ., s.a.
Br.M. IA. 41325
Boh. 814

A:— 5.

D:— 4: 8°; initials in MS.; officium B.M.V. in MS. bound in.

PSALTERIUM
s. loc.: s. typ., *c.* 1470/5
Stillwell P 947
Boh. 807

A:— 5, possibly 4.

D:— 4: 'Hoc . . . psalterium . . . habet suos psalmos, antiphonas, reponsoria, ymnos cum canticis . . . .' Each psalm is followed by gloria and response with space left free in between; also between the hymns some space is left free; however, it is doubtful whether the addition of musical notes was intended.

PSALTERIUM CUM HYMNIS
German?: s. typ., 1489
Paris BN. Rés. B. 2949

A:— 5.

236. PSALTERIUM ROMANUM
s. loc.: s. typ., *c.* 1490
Paris BN. Rés. Vél. 130

A:— 2; 6: throughout.

C:— 1: 1; 2: 8; 3: 4; 4: red; 5; 7b.

D:— 4: no colophon; *édition de luxe*; MS. notes very carefully written.

PSALTERIUM
Antwerp: s. typ., s.a.
Paris BN. Rés. A. 11012
Boh. 881

A:— 5.

D:— 4: on fols. 1a and b identical woodcuts.

PSALTERIUM
Antwerp: Eckert, *c.* 1500
Stillwell P 967
not in Boh.

A:— 5.

D:— 4: woodcut 'David and Goliath' on the title; see Nijhoff, *L'Art typographique*, part III, pl. 1; small 8°.

PSALTERIUM
Antwerp: Leeu, 1487
Br.M. IA. 49756

Cambridge UL., Oates 3890
Boh. 914
A:— 5.
D:— 4: title woodcut; 200 fols., small 8°.

PSALTERIUM
Antwerp: Leeu, 1488
Cambridge UL., Oates 3907
Boh. 916
A:— 5.
D:— 4: 102 fols., 8°.

PSALTERIUM
Antwerp: Leeu, 1490
Cambridge UL., Oates 3928
Boh. 923
A:— 5.
D:— 4: 240 fols., small 8°.

PSALTERIUM ULTRAJECTENSE
Antwerp: Leeu, 1491
Br.M. IA. 49831
Boh. 982
A:— 5.

PSALTERIUM LATINUM
Augsburg: Zainer, 1471/2
Br.M. IB. 5560
Oxf. Bodl. Auct. VI. Q. infra I. 11
Cambridge UL., Oates 886
Stillwell P 948
Boh. 832 and 833
A:— 5.
D:— 4: explicit translacio . . . psalterii
beatissimi Jeronimi eusebii; 2°; in Bohatta
listed as two different editions.

PSALTERIUM CUM HYMNIS
Augsburg: Ratdolt, c. 1490
Oxf. Bodl. Douce 268
Boh. 829
A:— 5.
D:— 4: initial with the figure of King David
playing the harp; 2°; not in Schottenloher.

237. PSALTERIUM
Bamberg: Sensenschmidt, c. 1482
Stillwell P 954
Boh. 835
A:— 3; 6: wherever needed.
C:— 1: 1; 3: 4; 4: red; 5; 7c(?).
D:— 4: between the psalms the staves occur
occasionally only; but throughout for the
canticles and hymns; in the copy MS. note
'Strassburg, Dumbach 1496'.

PSALTERIUM RATISPONENSE
Bamberg: Sensenschmidt and Petzen-
steiner, c. 1490
Stillwell P 969
Boh. 967
A:— 5.

238. PSALTERIUM
Basle: Wenssler, c. 1487
Stillwell P 957
Boh. 837a
A:— 3; 6: throughout between the psalms.
C:— 1: 1; 2: 6; 3: 4; 4: red; 5; 6: d(1); 7c.

PSALTERIUM
Beromünster: Helye de Louffen, c. 1470
Oxf. Bodl. Auct. M. infra II. 14
Paris BN. Rés. B. 1019
Boh. 866
A:— 5.

PSALTERIUM
Cologne: Homborch, c. 1475
Br.M. IA. 15633
Boh. 838; Lib. 67
A:— 5.
D:— 4: part of Hain 13464.

PSALTERIUM
Cologne: Homborch, c. 1479
Cambridge UL., Oates 670
Boh. 840; Voulliéme 986
A:— 5.
D:— 4: Printer in Oates: Conrad Wintens.

239. PSALTERIUM
Cologne: Homborch, c. 1482
Paris BN. Rés. B. 2787 and Vél. 923
Stillwell P 953
Boh. 883 and 839?
Voulliéme 987
A:— 4; 6: space is left free for one or two
rows of staves at the beginning of each
psalm; rubrics are added as in an Anti-
phonarium.
C:— 1: 1.
D:— 4: in B.N. Rés. B. 2787 occasionally
MS. notes.

PSALTERIUM
Cologne: Quentell, c. 1500
Stillwell P 966
Boh. 841; Voulliéme 990
A:— 5.
D:— 4: 16°.

PSALTERIUM
Cologne: Renschen, 1483
Br.M. IA. 5264
Boh. 954 or 955?
Voulliéme 988
A:— 5.
D:— 4: small 8⁰.

240. PSALTERIUM
Delft: Jacobzoen van der Meer, s.a.
Cambridge UL., Oates 3347
Boh. 843
A:— 4; 6: irregular spaces left free between
psalms.

PSALTERIUM
Deventer: Breda, 1494
Cambridge UL., Oates 3555
Boh. 925
A:— 5.
D:— 4: manc.; several parts, printed later and
in MS., bound in; small 8⁰.

PSALTERIUM
Eichstädt: Reyser, c. 1478
Oxf. Bodl. Auct. M. inf. II. 16
Boh. 844?
A:— 5.
D:— 4: following Boh. c. 1485?

PSALTERIUM LATINUM &
OFFICIUM
Ferrara: Magister Laurentius, 1497
Br.M. IA. 257 (55–56)
A:— 5.
D:— 4: 8⁰; some beautiful small woodcuts.

PSALTERIUM
Florence: apud S. Jacobum de Ripoli,
c. 1480
Paris Ars. 8⁰ T. 1959
Boh. 884
A:— 5.
D:— 4: 8⁰.

PSALTERIUM CUM HYMNIS
Florence: Bonaccorsi, 1489
Br.M. IB. 27734
Boh. 921; Lib. 68
A:— 5.

PSALTERIUM CUM CANTICIS
Ingolstadt: Printer of the Psalterium,
c. 1490

Br.M. IB. 13553
Cambridge UL., Oates 1325
Boh. 885?; Lib. 69
A:— 5.
D:— 4: Bohatta 'ante 1487'.

PSALTERIUM
Leipzig: Brandis, c. 1488
Stillwell P 958
Boh. 847
A:— 5.

PSALTERIUM
Leipzig: Kachelofen, 1485
Stillwell P 955
Boh. 911
A:— 5.

PSALTERIUM
Leipzig: Kachelofen, 1497
Br.M. IA. 12342
Cambridge UL., Oates 1283
Boh. 930; Lib. 70
A:— 5.

PSALTERIUM
Lübeck or Leipzig: s. typ., c. 1480/5
Oxf. Bodl. Auct. M. inf. T. 5
Boh. 856
A:— 5.
D:— 4: in the copy a slip attributing the book
to Pfister, Bamberg 1462.

PSALTERIUM
Lyons: Reinhard and Pistoris, c. 1480
Br.M. IA. 41571
Oxf. Bodl. Inc. f. F 2 $\left(\frac{1480}{1}\right)$
Stillwell P 952
Boh. 861
A:— 5.
D:— 4: 8⁰; all copies manc.; by Stillwell
attributed to Philippi and Reinhard.

PSALTERIUM
Magdeburg: Ghotan, 1481
Oxf. Bodl. Auct. VI. Q. IV. 38
Boh. 902; Proctor 2753
A:— 5.
D:— 4: the rubrics and the incipits of the
antiphons are added by hand in between
the psalms; Bohatta says that this book is
not identical with Proctor 2753.

241. PSALTERIUM
Mainz: Schoeffer, 1457
Paris BN. Rés. Vél. 223/4
Cambridge UL. frg., Oates 19
Boh. 894
A:— 4; 6: throughout.
C:— 1: 1; 2: 11; (3: 4 and 5 in MS.); 5.
D:— 4: lines and notes in MS.; Bohatta 'cum notis musicis'.

242. PSALTERIUM
Mainz: Schoeffer, 1459
Paris BN. Rés. Vél. 225/6
Stillwell P 970
Cambridge UL. frg., Oates 20
Boh. 949
A:— 4; 6: throughout.
C:— 1: 1, sometimes 2.
D:— 4: notes and staves MS.; the text underlying the music uses a smaller type, which is not used in the first part, and only from the hymn 'Iam lucis' on; the lines on the first 9 leaves drawn in red that differs from the initials, later in black; the measure of the spaces in the red and black staves differs.

PSALTERIUM
Mainz: ? Schoeffer; ? before 1470
Oxf. Bodl. Auct. M. inf. I. 11
Boh. 865
A:— 5.
D:— 4: in many places music added in MS. on top and bottom of pages.

243. PSALTERIUM
Mainz: Schoeffer, 1490
Paris BN. Rés. Vél. 227
Stillwell P 971, frg.
Br.M. IC. 258, frg.
Boh. 950
A:— 1; 6: throughout.
B:— 2; 3: 𝅘𝅥 𝅘𝅥𝅮 𝅘𝅥; 6 for the greater part stems.
C:— 1: 1, corresponding to the length of the text; 2: 10; 3: 4; 4: red; 5; 7c.
D:— 1: C and F 𝄐 9; 2: ✓; 3: bars between verses.

244. PSALTERIUM CONSTANTIENSE
Mainz: s. typ., 1500
Br.M. C. 52. g. 9
Boh. 958
A:— 1 and 3, even on one and the same page; 6: throughout.

B:— 2; 3: 𝅘𝅥 𝅘𝅥𝅮 𝅘𝅥𝅮; 5: straight, with small points; 6: both forms.
C:— 1: 1; 2: as many staves as are required by the text; 6: d (2, but not throughout).
D:— 1: C and F 𝄐 𝟛; 2: ✓; 3: bars occasionally; 4: title: Psalterium chorale cum suis antiphonis; collectis: precibus: et hymnis. Incipit secundum ritum ecclesie Constantiensis.

PSALTERIUM ROMANUM
Mantua: Schall, 1478?
Br.M. IA. 30655
Boh. 971
A:— 5.

PSALTERIUM
Merseburg: Lucas Brandis, 1470?
Oxf. Bodl. Auct. I. Q. VII. 74
Boh. 864
A:— 5.
D:— 4: from the monastery in Buxheim; antiphons added in MS.

PSALTERIUM CUM COMMENTARIO
Milan: s. typ., 1477
Br.M. IA. 26303
Oxf. Bodl. Auct. M. inf. T. 4
Stillwell P 950
Boh. 896 and 952
A:— 5.
D:— 4: before each psalm its 'titulus', and after it the 'oratio'; 340 fols.; attributed by Bohatta 896 to Valdarfer, and 952 to Vespolate; by British Museum to 'Printer of Psalterio in volgare'.

PSALTERIUM CUM HYMNIS
Milan: Pachel and Scinzenzeler, 1482
Br.M. IA. 26480
Oxf. Bodl. Auct. M. inf. I. 1
Boh. 974
A:— 5.

PSALTERIUM AMBROSIANUM
Milan: Pachel and Scinzenzeler, 1486
Br.M. IB. 26533
Stillwell P 968
Boh. 946; Lib. 73
A:— 5.
D:— 4: bound together with Magnificat, Milan: Zarotus, and Hymnarium, Milan: Pachel and Scinzenzeler.

PSALTERIUM
Naples: Alding and Bermentlo, 1476
Paris BN. Rés. B. 2788
Oxf. Bodl. Auct. M. inf. I. 10
Boh. 895
A:— 5.
D:— 4: contains Psalter and Antiphons.

PSALTERIUM
Naples: Moravus, 1478
Stillwell O 31
Boh. 898
A:— 5.
D:— 4: Psalmi penitentiales David cum Letanijs. This book starts with the officium B.M.V., and follows with the psalms and responses of the funeral rites; it is listed by Stillwell as Officium, and by Bohatta, *Liturgische Bibliographie*, no. 898, as Psalterium, and in his *Bibliographie des livres d'heures*, no. 35, as Officium.

PSALTERIUM ROMANUM
Naples: Polonia and Lucifero, 1478
Paris BN. Rés. B. 1609
Boh. 975?
A:— 5.
D:— 4: names of printers supplied from Fava; Bohatta 975 gives 1482 as date.

PSALTERIUM CUM HYMNIS ET
  CANTICIS ROMANUM
Naples: Riessinger, *c.* 1475
Paris Ars. 8° T. 1958
A:— 5.
D:— 4: text in antiqua, name of printer in gothic type; no psalterium by Riessinger listed in Fava.

245. PSALTERIUM
Nuremberg: Creussner, *c.* 1473
Oxf. Bodl. Auct. M. infra T. 3
Boh. 888 and 890 (?)
A:— 4; 6: irregular, between two songs.

246. PSALTERIUM ORD. PRAEDICA-
  TORUM
Nuremberg: Creussner, *c.* 1480
Br.M. IB. 7780
Stillwell P 951
Boh. 869 = 963
A:— 4; 6: space left free between the psalms, but not between the canticles.

247. PSALTERIUM ORD. PRAEDICA-
  TORUM
Nuremberg: Creussner, not after 1484
Br.M. IB. 7778
Oxf. Bodl. Auct. M. infra II. 1
Cambridge UL., Oates 1062
Boh. 889; Lib. 74
A:— 4; the openings of the melodies are given throughout in MS., like mottoes, in the British Museum copy.

PSALTERIUM
Nuremberg: Hochfeder, 1497
Br.M. IA. 8186
Boh. 933
A:— 5.
C:— 4: midget size, 1 × 2 in.

PSALTERIUM
Nuremberg: Koberger, 1471?
Br.M. IA. 7112
Boh. 870
A:— 5.

PSALTERIUM
Nuremberg: Koberger, 1494 and 1495
Oxf. Bodl. Auct. I. Q. 5. 19
Stillwell P 959
not in Boh.
A:— 5.
D:— 4: With the commentary of Bruno, Bishop of Würzburg.

PSALTERIUM
Nuremberg: Koberger, 1497
Oxf. Bodl. Auct. 5. Q. 76
Stillwell P 965
A:— 5.
D:— 4: Almost identical with the preceding item.

PSALTERIUM CUM CANTICIS ET
  HYMNIS
Nuremberg: Sensenschmidt and Frisner,
  c. 1470
Oxf. Bodl. Auct. Q. sup. III. 5
Boh. 871
A:— 5.

PSALTERIUM CUM HYMNIS
Paris: Caillaut, 1488
Cambridge UL., Oates 2931
Boh. 918
A:— 5.
D:— 4: contains psalms, litanies, canticles, and hymns; 16 woodcut illustrations.

248. PSALTERIUM CUM HYMNIS
Paris: Gering and Rembolt, 1494
Paris BN. Rés. Vél. 1619
Paris SG. OE. 15. 805, cat. 719
Boh. 962
A:— 1; 6: throughout.
B:— 1; 3: ♩ ♩ ♩ ♩ ♩; 5: straight; 6: no stems.
C:— 1: 1; 2: 7 and 8; 3: 4; 4: red: 5; 7c.
D:— 1: C and F 〔 〕 § and 〔 ♮; 2: ♩; 3: red bars between sentences; 4: following Explicit on fol. E6, a supplement with antiphons; the form of the ligatures in the first part (a–z) differs from the forms in the second part starting with quire A.

PSALTERIUM DIVE VIRGINIS
    MARIE
Paris: Jehannot (?), *c. 1495*
Washington, Library of Congress
Boh. 872?
A:— 5.
D:— 4: paraphrases of psalms listed in the order of the 'hours'; borders as in the *livres d'heures*.

PSALTERIUM INTEMERATE DEI
    GENITRICIS
Paris: Kerver, 1497
Paris Maz. 961, cat., p. 518
A:— 5.
D:— 4: small 8º; printer's sign at the beginning; ornamented borders; at the end one leaf 'antiphonae de conceptione b.M.V.'

PSALTERIUM CUM HYMNIS
Paris: de la Barre pro Regnault, 1500
Oxf. Bodl. Gough Missal 70
Boh. 943
A:— 5.
D:— 4: printer's sign on the title.

PSALTERIUM
Paris: Levet, 1488
Br.M. IA. 39901
Cambridge UL., Oates 2982
Boh. 919
A:— 5.
D:— 4: *édition de luxe*, several woodcuts.

PSALTERIUM
Paris: Maynial and Gering, 1480
Oxf. Bodl. Douce 9
Boh. 899

A:— 5.
D:— 4: in antiqua; small 4º.

PSALTERIUM CISTERCIENSE
Speyer: Drach, 1486
Stillwell P 971
Boh. 876
A:— 5.
D:— 4: pocket size.

249. PSALTERIUM
Speyer?: s. typ., *c. 1490*
Oxf. Bodl. Auct. I. Q. III. 18
Boh. 810
A:— 3; 6: throughout.
C:— 1: 1; 2: 6; 3: 4; 4: red.
D:— 4: in some places guides are printed in the margin; they have the form of a musical ligature ♫; the second part of the book is an Hymnarium; the third part, in MS., contains text and music for the offices; the rubrics refer to 'sorores' (fol. 36b) and use the dialect form 'antiffen'; the book probably comes from a Dutch convent.

PSALTERIUM
Strasbourg: Rusch, *c. 1495*
Stillwell P 962
Boh. 825
A:— 5.

PSALTERIUM
Strasbourg: Rusch, *c. 1495*
Br.M. IA. 15633
Stillwell P 961
Boh. 828
A:— 5.
D:— 4: the British Museum copy is listed today as 'possibly German'; in the American copy in the Huntington Library a MS. note says 'Moguntiae Schoeffer 1485'.

250. PSALTERIUM CUM HYMNIS
Strasbourg: Pruess, *c. 1495*
Washington, Library of Congress
not in Stillwell
Boh. 826?
A:— 2; 6: throughout.
C:— 1: 1; 2: 7, however, there is nowhere a complete page; 3: 4; 4: red; 5; 7c.

251. PSALTERIUM
Strasbourg: Pruess, *c. 1498*
Br.M. IB. 1748
Boh. 948?; Lib. 75

A:— 2; 6: throughout.
C:— 1: 1; 2: 6 and 7; 3: 4; 4: red; 5; 7a.

PSALTERIUM
Treviso: Manzolo, s.a.
Cambridge UL., Oates 2458
A:— 5.
D:— 4: 111 fols., 8°.

PSALTERIUM
Ulm: Dinckmut, 1485/6
Br.M. IB. 9395
A:— 5.

PSALTERIUM CUM HYMNIS ET
  CANTICIS
Venice: Girardengus, 1482
Oxf. Bodl. Auct. T. inf. III. 12 vellum
Boh. 904
A:— 5.

PSALTERIUM
Venice: Hamman, 1496
Stillwell P 964
Boh. 928
A:— 5.
D:— 4: on the title 'Psalmista secundum morem curie Romane'; fol. 108b ss. 'hymnarius'; the set-up follows the cursus and is similar to a breviary.

PSALTERIUM
Venice: Petri, 1480
Paris BN. Rés. Vél. 1457
Boh. 893
A:— 5.
D:— 4: pocket edition.

PSALTERIUM
Venice: di Pietro, c. 1475
Br.M. IA. 19954
Stillwell P 949
Boh. 892; Lib. 76
A:— 5.

PSALTERIUM
Venice: Ragazonibus, 1488
Paris BN. Rés. B. 1610
Boh. 976
A:— 5.

PSALTERIUM
Venice: Siliprandis, 1478
Br.M. IA. 20704
Cambridge UL., Oates 1785
Paris BN. Rés. Vél. 1455
Boh. 972; Lib. 78
A:— 5.

PSALTERIUM ORD. PRAEDICA-
  TORUM
Venice: Spira, s.a.
Br.M. IA. 24216
Boh. 964; Lib. 81
A:— 5.
D:— 4: Bohatta 'c. 1490'.

PSALTERIUM
Venice: Spira, s.a.
Br.M. IA. 24254
Boh. 979?; Lib. 80
A:— 5.
D:— 4: Bohatta '1496'.

PSALTERIUM
Venice: Spira, 1495/6
Stillwell P 963
Boh. 927
A:— 5.
D:— 4: midget size, 1×2 in.

PSALTERIUM
Venice: Spira, 1499
Br.M. IA. 24239
Lib. 79
A:— 5.

PSALTERIUM
Venice: Tortis?, 1495
Br.M. IA. 25172
Stillwell P 960
Boh. 926; Lib. 77
A:— 5.
D:— 4: contains psalterium, hymni, letanie, officium feriarum.

PSALTERIUM CUM CANTICIS ET
  HYMNIS
Venice: de Zanchis?, s.a.
Oxf. Bodl. Auct. I. Q. VI. 26
A:— 5.
D:— 4: pocket edition; Bohatta 926 mixes up this item with the previous number.

PSALTERIUM IN USUM ANGLIAE
Westminster: Caxton, 1480
Br.M. IA. 55038
Boh. 947
A:— 5.

252. PSALTERIUM
Würzburg: Reyser, s.a.
Br.M. IC. 10525
Boh. 845?; Lib. 82

A:— 2 and 3; 6: throughout.

C:— 1: 1; 2: 10 and 11; 3: 4; 4: red; 6: a, d(1); 7b.

D:— 4: according to the note to GK. 5356 the Psalterium by Reyser should be a separate edition of the psalter section of his Breviarium Herbipolense; this is not probable for the edition above, because we should then not have staves; moreover, the signatures in our psalter do not agree with the quires in the Breviaria Herbipolensia, GK. 5356 sqq.

PSALTERIUM CUM CANTICIS
Würzburg: Reyser, *c*. 1485
Stillwell P 956
Boh. 846?

A:— 5.

D:— 4: No music is intended, though on some leaves spaces are left free; but this has been done so that the original text may correspond to the commentary.

PSALTERIUM BEATAE MARIAE VIRGINIS
Zinna: Cistercian monastery, *c*. 1493
Br.M. IA. 14703
Stillwell N 230

A:— 5.

PSALTERIUM
Zwolle: de Os, 1480
Br.M. IC. 35
Boh. 900

A:— 5.

D:— 4: manc.; bound together with a 'De virtute psalmorum' by St. Augustine; complete copy Campbell 539.

REGULE indicantes ordinem cujuslibet diei, Strasbourg, 1477
See Ordinarium Argentinense.

253. RESPONSORIA DEFUNCTORUM
Montserrat: Luschner, 1500
Br.M. K. 8. f. 18
Haebler 573 (5)

A:— 1; 6: throughout.

B:— 1; 3: ♪ ♩ ♫ and the usual forms, for a great part 4; 5: straight, no points; 6: no stems.

C:— 1: 1; 2: 3; 3: 4; 4: red; 5; 7a.

D:— 1: C and F ⌊ ♩⌠; 2: ♩; 3: bars between words; 4: manc.; small 4°; called in the Br.M. cat. 'Antiphoners—Benedic-

tines of Valladolid'; denoted by Haebler as Responsoriale.

254. RITUALE ROMANUM
Bologna: de Odis, 1487
Br.M. IA. 28858
Stillwell R 195
Boh. 723

A:— 1; 6: throughout.

B:— 1; 4; 5: straight, no points; 6: with stems.

C:— 1: 1; 2: 4; 3: 4; 4: red; 5; 7c.

D:— 1: C ⌊ and F ⌊♪ and ♩⌠; 2: ⌊; 3: bars between sentences occasionally; 4: listed in Bohatta as Liber catechumeni, in none of the copies is the book called Rituale, either in the title or in the colophon.

RITUALE AMBROSIANUM
See Ordinarium officii.

RITUALE ROMANUM
See Benedictionale Lubicense.

255. VIGILIAE AUGUSTENSES
Augsburg: Ratdolt, 1491
Br.M. IB. 6720
Boh. 1090; Lib. 83

A:— 1; 6: throughout.

B.— 2; 3: ♫ ♩; 6: stems in the loose ligatures.

C:— 1: 1; 2: 8; 3: 4; 4: red; 5; 7a.

D:— 1: C and F ℭ ⌠; 2: ∽; 3: bars between words; 4: Facs. Molitor, pl. 13.

256. VIGILIAE COLONIENSES
Cologne: Renschen, s.a.
Br.M. IA. 4473
Boh. 1091; Lib. 84
Voulliéme 1244

A:— 4; 6: throughout.

C:— 1: short passages introduced in the text.

D:— 4: at the end several pages in MS. with notes; Bohatta '*c*. 1480'.

257. VIGILIAE MAGUNTINAE
Basle: Wenssler, 1488
Cambridge UL., Oates 2748
Boh. 1095

A:— 1; 6: throughout, in the Cambridge copy in MS. from fol. 51b on.

B:— 2; 3: ♫♩♪ and the usual forms; 5: small points; 6: both forms.

C:— 1: 1; 2: 5; 3: 4; 4: red; 6: d(2); 7c.

D:— 1: C and F ε $\frac{3}{2}$; 2: ¢ ; 3: bars occasionally between sentences.

VIGILIAE
Paris: Vérard, *c.* 1497
Paris BN. Rés. Vél. 2237

A:— 5.

D:— 4: text in Latin and French.

VIGILIAE
Paris: Le Vostre, s.a.
Paris BN. Rés. B. 4427

A:— 5.

D:— 4: French text 'Les vigilles des mors' added.

CHRONOLOGICAL LIST

THE chronological list includes *all* liturgical incunabula in which printed music might be expected. For the dates, generally, the standard catalogues and bibliographies have been followed. It should be realized, however, that in many cases these are only approximate. The purpose of the list is to give a survey of the whole material, and to show the concentration and shifting of activities from one place to another, and from one shop to another; it also indicates which items are in this catalogue.

Date	Title	Place and Printer		Weale–Bohatta no.	This list
1457	Psalterium	Mainz	Schoeffer	894	no. 241
1459	Psalterium	Mainz	Schoeffer	949	no. 242
before 1470	Psalterium	Mainz	Schoeffer	865	p. 42
c. 1470	Psalterium	s.l.	s. typ.	807	p. 39
	Psalterium	Beromünster	Helye de Louffen	866	p. 40
	Psalterium	Merseburg	L. Brandis	864	p. 42
	Psalterium	Nuremberg	Sensenschmidt and Frisner	871	p. 43
	Psalterium	Strasbourg	? s. typ.	824	
c. 1471	Psalterium	Augsburg	Zainer	832/3	p. 40
	Psalterium	Nuremberg	Koberger	870	p. 43
c. 1473	Psalterium	Ulm	Zainer	878	
	Psalterium	Nuremberg	Creussner	888, 890?	no. 245
c. 1474	Ceremoniale	Marienthal	Fratres Comm.	557	p. 3
	Psalterium	Basle	Wenssler	837	p. 40
1474	Miss. Romanum	Milan	Zarotus	852	
after 1474	Ceremoniale	Marienthal	Fratres Comm.	—	p. 3
	Ordinarium	Marienthal	Fratres Comm.	756	p. 37
c. 1475	Miss. Slevicense	Schleswig	Arndes	1466	p. 29
	Ordinarium	Cologne	Goetz	759	
	Psalterium	Augsburg	Schoensperger	831	
	Psalterium	Cologne	Homborch	838	p. 40
	Psalterium	Lübeck	Ghotan	859	
	Psalterium	Würzburg	Reyser	846	
	Psalterium	Naples	Riessinger	—	p. 43
	Psalterium	Venice	di Pietro	892	p. 45
	Sequentiae	Cologne	Koelhof	1060	
1475	Directorium	Augsburg	s. typ.	569	
	Miss. Ambrosianum	Milan	Zarotus	26	no. 34
	Miss. Benedict. Bursf.	see Ceremoniale 1474		1679	
	Miss. Romanum	Rome	Han	853	
	Psalterium	Strasbourg	Flach	827	
after 1475	Psalterium	Würzburg	Reyser	845?	
c. 1476	Directorium Const.	s.l.	s. typ.	575	p. 4
	Graduale	Augsburg?	Zainer?	699	no. 15
1476	Hymni	Cologne	Koelhof	707	
	Litanie	Milan	Ungardus	—	p. 7
	Miss. Romanum	Milan	Zarotus	854	no. 118
	Miss. Romanum	Rome	Han	855	no. 119
	Psalterium	Naples	Alding, &c.	895	p. 43
	Rituale	Florence	Francisci	1053	

Date	Title	Place and Printer		Weale–Bohatta no.	This list
c. 1477	Miss. Romanum	Venice	Siliprandis	856	no. 120
	Miss. Romanum	Naples	Moravus	857	no. 121
	Ordinarium	Strasbourg	Pruess	754?	p. 37
	Psalterium Cist.	Milan	Printer of Psalt. in volg ?	896 = 952	p. 42
c. 1477/80	Ordinarium (Rituale)	Milan	s. typ.	1047	
c. 1478	Ordinarium Sarum	Westminster	Caxton	772	p. 37
	Psalterium	Eichstädt	Reyser	see c. 1485	
	Psalterium	Mantua	Schall	809; 971	p. 42
1478	Miss. Romanum	Milan	Zarotus	858	
	Psalterium	Messina	Alding	897	
	Psalterium	Naples	Moravus	898 (= no. 35 of *Livres d'heures*)	p. 42
	Psalterium	Naples	Polonus, &c.	975	p. 43
	Psalterium	Venice	Jenson	973	
	Psalterium	Venice	Siliprandis	972	p. 45
c. 1479	Psalterium	s.l.	s. typ.	821	
	Psalterium	Cologne	Homborch	840	p. 40
1479	Miss. Parisiense	s.l.	s. typ.	698	
	Miss. Pragense	Pilsen	s. typ.	795	p. 19
	Miss. Romanum	Venice	s. typ.	859	no. 122
	Miss. Romanum	Milan	Zarotus	860	no. 123
	Miss. Romanum	s.l.	s. typ.	861	
c. 1480	Agenda	Pilsen	Printer of Miss. Pragense	—	p. 2
	Collectarium				see c. 1485
	Graduale			699	see c. 1476
	Miss. Basiliense	Basle	Wenssler	153	no. 44
	Psalterium	s.l.	s. typ.	817, 820, 822	
	Psalterium	Florence	Ripoli	884	p. 41
	Psalterium	Leipzig or Lübeck	s. typ.	856	p. 41
	Psalterium	Lübeck	L. Brandis	857	
	Psalterium	Lübeck	Snell	860	
	Psalterium	Lyons	Reinhart, &c.	861	p. 41
	Psalterium	Nuremberg or Bamberg		867/8	
	Psalterium	Nuremberg	Creussner	869, 963	no. 246
	Psalterium	Paris	s. typ.	872	
	Psalterium	Reutlingen	Greiff	873	
	Psalterium	Rome	Silber	874	
	Psalterium	Venice	s. typ.	969	
	Vigiliae	Cologne	Renschen	1091	no. 256
1480	Agenda	Mainz	Numeister	13	p. 1
	Hymni	Cologne	Koelhof	708	p. 6
	Miss. Basiliense	Basle	Richel	154	no. 45
	Miss. Herbipolense	Würzburg	Reyser	427	
	Miss. Hildensemense	Magdeburg	Ghotan	446	
	Miss. Magdeburgense	Magdeburg	M. Brandis	569	p. 16
	Miss. Messanense	Messina	Alding	592	
	Miss. Romanum	Milan	Pachel. &c.	864	no. 124
	Miss. Strigonense	Verona	s. typ.	1488	
	Miss. Ultramontense	Verona	s. typ.	1607	

Date	Title	Place and Printer		Weale–Bohatta no.	This list
1480	Psalterium	s.l.	s. typ.	814	p. 39
	Psalterium	Milan	Pedemonte	959	
	Psalterium	Paris	Gering, &c.	899	
	Psalterium	Zwolle	de Os	900	p. 46
	Psalterium	Venice	Britannicis	901	
	Psalterium	Venice	Petri	893	p. 45
	Psalterium	Westminster	Caxton	947	p. 45
not after 1480	Miss. Constantiense	Basle	Richel	306	no. 64
c. 1481	Psalterium	Venice	Wild	880	
1481	Directorium	Basle	Wenssler	577	
	Miss. Benedictinum	Bamberg	Sensenschmidt	1680	no. 207
	Miss. Coloniense	Cologne	Homborch	286	no. 60
	Miss. Herbipolense	Würzburg	Reyser	428	no. 75
	Miss. Parisiense	Paris	Dupré, &c.	699	no. 96
	Miss. Romanum	Venice	s. typ.	865	
	Miss. Romanum	Venice	Tortis	866	
	Miss. Romanum	Milan	Pachel, &c.	867	
	Miss. Romanum	Milan	Zarotus	868	
	Miss. Romanum	Paris	Dupré	869	
	Miss. Romanum	Venice	O. Scotus	870	nos. 12/56
	Miss. Romanum	Venice	Renner	871	p. 21
	Miss. Virdunense	Paris	Dupré	1636	no. 202
	Psalterium	Magdeburg	Ghotan	902	p. 41
	Psalterium	Milan	Pachel, &c.	903 = 974?	
c. 1482	Psalterium	Bamberg	Sensenschmidt	835	no. 237
	Psalterium	Cologne	Homborch	883 = 839?	no. 239
1482	Agenda	Würzburg	Reyser	7	no. 3
	Compendium	Venice	Francfordia	564/5	p. 4
	Directorium	Basle	Wenssler	578	
	Miss. Ambrosianum	Milan	Valdarfer	27	no. 35
	Miss. Carnotense	Chartres	Dupré	234	no. 54
	Miss. Coloniense	Cologne	Homborch	287	
	Miss. Moguntinum	Würzburg	Reyser	622	no. 56
	Miss. Nannentense	Venice	Alexander, &c.	661	
	Miss. Praedicatorum	Milan	Zarotus	—	no. 211
	Miss. Praedicatorum	Venice	O. Scotus	1815	no. 212
	Miss. Romanum	Rome	Planck	872	
	Miss. Romanum	Naples	Moravus	873	
	Miss. Romanum	Venice	Alexander	874	
	Miss. Romanum	Venice	O. Scotus	875	
	Miss. Romanum	s.l.	s. typ.	876	
	Miss. Romanum	Venice	O. Scotus	877	no. 127
	Miss. Romanum	Venice	de Forlino, &c.	878	
	Miss. Romanum	Venice	s. typ.	879	
	Miss. Romanum	Venice	Torresanus	880	
	Psalterium	Milan	Pachel, &c.	974	p. 42
	Psalterium	Naples	s. typ.	975	see 1478
c. 1483	Miss. Romanum	Albi	Numeister	881	no. 128
	Miss. Romanum	Venice	Ratdolt	882	
	Psalterium	Basle	Amerbach	836	
1483	Compendium	Venice	Francfordia	564	see 1482
	Compendium Romanum	Venice	Torresanus, &c.	—	p. 4
	Miss. Lemovicense	Paris	Dupré	496	
	Miss. Ottoniense	Lübeck	L. Brandis	693	
	Miss. Praedicatorum	Naples	Moravus	1816	no. 213

Date	Title	Place	and Printer	Weale–Bohatta no.	This list
1483	Miss. Romanum	Milan	Pachel, &c.	883	
	Miss. Romanum	Venice	Benaliis, &c.	884	no. 129
	Miss. Romanum	Cologne	Renschen	885	
	Miss. Romanum	Nuremberg	s. typ.	886	
	Miss. Romanum (slavonice)	Venice	Torresanus	1330	p. 22
	Miss. Vratislaviense	Mainz	Schoeffer	1653	p. 31
	Psalterium	Cologne	Renschen	954, 955	p. 40
	Psalterium	Paris	Gering	905	
c. 1484	Ordinarium Leodiense	Brussels	Fratres Comm.	764/5	
	Psalterium	Magdeburg	Koch	863	
c. 1484–9	Psalterium	Antwerp?	s. typ.	823	
1484	Directorium	Augsburg	Baemler	570	
	Directorium	Basle	Wenssler	574	p. 4
	Miss. Cracoviense	Mainz	Schoeffer	326	p. 13
	Miss. Herbipolense	Würzburg	Reyser	430	no. 76
	Miss. Praedicatorum	Venice	Francfordia	1817	no. 214
	Miss. Romanum	Venice	Benaliis	888	no. 129
	Miss. Romanum	Venice	Arrivabene, &c.	889	no. 132
	Miss. Romanum	Nuremberg	Stuchs	890	p. 22
	Miss. Romanum	Venice	Girardengus	891/891a	nos. 131/2
	Miss. Romanum	Venice	Francfordia	892	
	Miss. Spirense	Speyer	Drach	1481	
	Miss. Strigonense	Nuremberg	Koberger	1490	
	Miss. Upsalense				see before 1487
	Obsequiale Frisingense	Bamberg	Sensenschmidt	749	p. 35
	Psalterium	Cologne	Renschen	906	
	Psalterium	Ghent	de Keysere	907	
not after 1484	Psalterium	Nuremberg	Creussner	889	no. 247
before 1485	Miss. Basiliense	Basle	Wenssler	155	no. 46
c. 1485	Collectarium	Bamberg	Sensenschmidt	560/1	pp. 3–4
	Agenda (Benedictionale)	Lübeck	M. Brandis	8	no. 13
	Miss. Basiliense	Basle	Wenssler?	156?	p. 11
	Ordinarium	Lübeck	M. Brandis	770 (769?)	no. 228a
	Psalterium	Bamberg	Sensenschmidt		see c. 1490
	Psalterium	Cologne	Renschen	954	
	Psalterium	Eichstädt	Reyser	844	p. 41
	Psalterium	Milan	Zarotus	945	
	Psalterium	Würzburg	Reyser	846?	p. 46
not before 1485	Psalterium	Lübeck	Ghotan	887	
c. 1485–6	Psalterium	Ulm	Dinckmut	—	p. 45
	Sequentiae & Hymni	Deventer	Breda	1058	
1485	Miss. Basiliense	Basle	Kesler	157	
	Miss. Bisuntinense	Salins	Bigot, &c.	174	p. 11
	Miss. Caesaraugust.	Zaragossa	Hurus	218 = 691	1488
	Miss. Constantiense	Basle	Kollicker	307	no. 65
	Miss. Lemovicense	s. l.	s. typ.	497	
	Miss. Misniense	Mainz	Schoeffer	609	
	Miss. Ratisponense	Bamberg	Sensenschmidt	806	no. 110
	Miss. Romanum	Basle	Kesler	893 see 1485 Miss. Basiliense	
	Miss. Romanum	Lyons	Hus	894	no. 135
	Miss. Romanum	Venice	Petrus Cremonensis	895	p. 23

Date	Title	Place and Printer		Weale–Bohatta no.	This list
1485	Miss. Romanum	Venice	Paltasichis	896	no. 136
	Miss. Romanum	Venice	Francfordia	897	
	Miss. Turonense	Tours	Dupré	1594	
	Ordinarium Prae-monstratense	Lübeck	M. Brandis	771?	no. 228b
	Pontificale	Rome	Planck	777	no. 229
	Psalterium	Leipzig	M. Brandis	908	
	Psalterium	Leipzig	Kachelofen	909/11	p. 41
c. 1486	Manuale Caesar-augustanum	Hijar	Cordoba	—	p. 8
1486	Agenda Olomucensis	Brünn	Stahel, &c.	14	
	Hymnarium	Milan	Pachel, &c.	946	no. 22
	Magnificat	Milan	Zarotus	—	no. 24
	Miss. Ambrosianum	Milan	Pachel, &c.	28	
	Miss. Ambrosianum	Milan	Zarotus	29	
	Miss. Eystedtense	Eichstädt	Reyser	388	p. 14
	Miss. Leodiense	Cologne	Renschen	508	
	Miss. Lubicense	Lübeck	M. Brandis	542	
	Miss. Magdeburgense	Magdeburg	Koch	570	p. 16
	Miss. Moguntinum	Basle	Wenssler	623	
	Miss. Slevicense	Schleswig	Arndes		see c. 1475
	Miss. Strigonense	Venice	Ratdolt	1492	
	Ordinarium	Cologne	Koelhof	762	p. 37
	Psalterium	s.l.	s. typ.	912	
	Psalterium	Cluny	Wenssler		see c. 1493
	Psalterium	Milan	Pachel, &c.	946	p. 42
	Psalterium Cisterc.	Speyer	Drach	876	p. 44
	Psalterium	Venice	de Ballis	913	
before 1487	Miss. Upsalense	s.l.	s. typ.	1609	no. 202
	Psalterium	Ingolstadt	s. typ.		see c. 1490
c. 1487	Agenda pro mortuis	Bamberg	Sensenschmidt	—	no. 8
	Miss. Vratislavense	Strasbourg	Pruess	1655	no. 204
	Psalterium	Basle	Wenssler	837a	no. 236
1487	Benedictionale	Leipzig	M. Brandis	31	
	Hymni	Paris	Levet	712?	p. 7
	Liber catechumeni	Bologna			see Rituale
	Miss. Ambianense	Paris	s. typ.	12	no. 33
	Miss. Cisterciense	Strasbourg	Grüninger	1751	p. 33
	Miss. Cisterciense	Paris	s. typ.	1752	
	Miss. Coloniense	Basle	Wenssler	288	no. 61
	Miss. Cracoviense	Mainz	Schoeffer	327/8	
	Miss. Fratrum Minorum	s.l.	s. typ.	1913	no. 221
	Miss. Frisingense	Bamberg	Sensenschmidt	395	no. 69
	Miss. Lugdunense	Lyons	Numeister	546/7	no. 86
	Miss. Marchicum	s.l.	s. typ.	577	
	Miss. Parisiense	Venice	Hamman	700	no. 97
	Miss. Praedicatorum	Venice	Bevilaqua	1818	
	Miss. Romanum	Venice	Paganinis	899	
	Miss. Romanum	Venice	Francfordia	900	no. 137
	Miss. Romanum	Basle	Wenssler	901	
	Miss. Sarum	Paris	Maynial/Caxton	1387	
	Miss. Spirense	Bamberg	Sensenschmidt, &c.	1482	no. 187
	Miss. Strengense	Lübeck	Ghotan	1486	no. 188
	Obsequiale	Augsburg	Ratdolt	742/3	no. 222

Date	Title	Place and Printer		Weale–Bohatta no.	This list
1487	Ordinarium Leodiense	Brussels	Fratres Comm.	766	
	Ordinarium Sarum	Westminster	Caxton	773	p. 37
	Psalterium	Antwerp	Leeu	914	p. 39
	Psalterium	Milan	Zarotus	915	
	Rituale	Bologna	de Odis	723?	no. 254
	Sequentiae	Antwerp	Leeu	1062	
c. 1488	Miss. Treverense	Basle	Wenssler	1575	no. 197
	Miss. Wormatiense	Basle	Wenssler	1649	no. 205
	Ordinarium	s.l.	s. typ.	770	
	Psalterium	Leipzig	M. Brandis	847	p. 41
	Psalterium	Zwolle	de Os	877	
1488	Agenda Argentinensis	Basle	Wenssler	3	no. 1
	Compendium	Venice	Torresanus, &c.	562	p. 4
	Directorium Sarum	Antwerp	Leeu	585	p. 5
	Graduale	Basle	Wenssler	701/2	no. 16
	Hymni	Paris	Caillaut	713	see 1492
	Miss. Aboense	Lübeck	Ghotan	1	no. 32
	Miss. Ambrosianum	Milan	Zarotus	30	
	Miss. Andegavense	Paris	s. typ.	54	
	Miss. Basiliense	Basle	Wenssler	158	no. 47
	Miss. Caesaraugustanum	Zaragossa	Hurus	691	no. 52
	Miss. Legionense	Salamanca	s. typ.	495	
	Miss. Moguntinum	Basle	Wenssler	625 (624?)	no. 88
	Miss. Olomucense	Bamberg	Drach	688	
	Miss. Parisiense	Paris	Vérard	701	
	Miss. Pictaviense	Poitiers	Bouyer	781	
	Miss. Praedicatorum	Lübeck	Ghotan	1820	
	Miss. Romanum	Milan	Zarotus	902	no. 138
	Miss. Romanum	Milan	Pachel	903	
	Miss. Romanum	Venice	Hamman	904	no. 139
	Miss. Romanum	Rome	Planck	905	no. 140
	Miss. Sagiense	Rouen	Le Talleur	1371	no. 173
	Miss. Toletanum	Venice	s. typ.	1529	
	Obsequiale	Eichstädt	Reyser	748	no. 225
	Ordinarium Sarum	Antwerp	Leeu	585	see Directorium
	Psalterium	Antwerp	Leeu	916	p. 39
	Psalterium	Nuremberg	Stuchs	917	
	Psalterium	Paris	Caillaut	918	p. 43
	Psalterium	Paris	Levet	919/20	p. 44
	Psalterium	Venice	Ragazonibus	976	p. 45
	Vigiliae	Basle	Wenssler	1095	no. 257
c. 1489	Miss. Sarum	Basle	Wenssler	1388	no. 177
1489	Directorium	Westminster	Caxton	584?	p. 5
	Manuale Neapolitanum	Naples	s. typ.	734	
	Miss. Andegavense	Paris	Higman and Hopyl	55	no. 37
	Miss. Augustanum	Bamberg	Sensenschmidt	103	
	Miss. Carnotense	s.l.	s. typ.	235	
	Miss. Cathalaunense	Paris	Dupré	253	no. 56
	Miss. Cenomanense	Rouen	Le Talleur	258	
	Miss. Eystettiense	Eichstädt	Reyser	389	
	Miss. Monasteriense	Cologne	Renschen	641	no. 91
	Miss. Parisiense	Paris	Dupré	702	no. 98
	Miss. Parisiense	Paris	Dupré	703	nos. 99/101
	Miss. Pragense	Bamberg	Sensenschmidt	796	no. 108
	Miss. Romanum	Venice	Tortis	907	no. 141
	Miss. Romanum	Venice	de Pennis	908	

Date	Title	Place and	Printer	Weale–Bohatta no.	This list
1489	Miss. Romanum	Venice	Ragazonibus	909	
	Miss. Romanum	s.l.	s. typ.	910/11	
	Obsequiale	Augsburg	Ratdolt	—	no. 223
	Ordinarium	Strasbourg	s. typ.	755	
	Psalterium	s.l. German?	s. typ.	—	p. 39
	Psalterium	Florence	Bonaccorsi	921	p. 41
	Psalterium	Lyons	Numeister	922	
	Psalterium Aeduense	Paris	Seigneret	944	
	Psalterium Argentinum	Strasbourg	Grüninger	948	
c. 1490	Agenda Moguntinensis	Strasbourg	Pruess	12	no. 5
	Hymnarium	Deventer	Pafraet	710	p. 7
	Miss. Argentinense	Strasbourg	Pruess	88	no. 39
	Miss. Romanum	Venice	s. typ.	912	no. 142
	Miss. Speciale	Strasbourg	Ratdolt	1472	
	Ordinarium	Cologne	Quentell	760	
	Ordinarium	Cologne	Zell	761	
	Psalterium	s.l.	s. typ.	—	no. 236
	Psalterium	Speyer?	s. typ.	810	no. 249
	Psalterium	Augsburg	Ratdolt	829	p. 46
	Psalterium	Bamberg	Sensenschmidt, &c.	967	p. 46
	Psalterium	Ingolstadt	s. typ.	885	p. 41
	Psalterium	Venice	Ragazonibus	970	
	Psalterium	Venice	Spira	964	p. 45
1490	Agenda Patavensis	Passau	Petri	16	no. 6
	Directorium	Augsburg	Baemler	571 (= 572 = 1495?)	
	Manuale Carnotense	Paris	Maynial	728	no. 25
	Miss. Ambrosianum	Milan	Zarotus	31	
	Miss. Autissiodorense	Paris	Dupré	124	no. 41
	Miss. Bambergense	Bamberg	Sensenschmidt, &c.	130	no. 42
	Miss. Carmelitorum	Brescia	Boninis	1884	no. 219
	Miss. Carnotense	Paris	Higman	236	no. 55
	Miss. Cenomanense	Rouen	Morin	259	
	Miss. Gebennense	Geneva	Faber	400	
	Miss. Halberstadtense	Augsburg	Ratdolt	417	no. 73
	Miss. Humilitorum	Milan	Zarotus	1800	no. 209
	Miss. Nivernense	Paris	Dupré	676	no. 94
	Miss. Parisiense				see 1489
	Miss. Romanum	Lyons	Giboletus	843	no. 117
	Miss. Romanum	Venice	Sessa	914	no. 143
	Miss. Strigonense	Nuremberg	Stuchs	1493	
	Miss. Tolosanum	Toulouse	Cleblat	1539	
	Miss. Upsalense				see before 1487
	Miss. Valentinense	s.l.	s. typ.	1614	
	Miss. Xantonense	Paris	s. typ.	1662	p. 32
	Psalterium	Antwerp	Leeu	923	p. 39
	Psalterium	Mainz	Schoeffer	950	p. 39
	Psalterium	Venice	Ragazonibus	977	
	Sequentiae	Deventer	Breda	1063	
c. 1491	Antiphonarium	Seville	Comp. Alemanos	25	no. 10
	Miss. Redonense	Poitiers	Bouyer, &c.	817	no. 115
1491	Agenda Argentinensis	Strasbourg	Schott	2	
	Agenda Bambergensis	Bamberg	Petzensteiner, &c.	5	no. 2

Date	Title	Place and Printer		Weale–Bohatta no.	This list
1491	Hymni	Deventer	Pafraet	714	
	Miss. Auscitanum	Lyons	de Cossis	119	
	Miss. Atrebatense	Paris	Dupré	93	
	Miss. Augustense	Augsburg	Ratdolt	104	
	Miss. Bambergense	Bamberg	Sensenschmidt, &c.	131	
	Miss. Eremitarum	Nuremberg	Stuchs	1804	
	Miss. Gebennense	Geneva	Faber	401	no. 71
	Miss. Herbipolense	Würzburg	Reyser	432	no. 77
	Miss. Laudunense	Paris	Dupré	483	no. 81
	Miss. Lingonense	Paris	Dupré	535	p. 16
	Miss. Morinense	Paris	Dupré	—	no. 92
	Miss. Parisiense	Paris	Higman	704	no. 102
	Miss. Pataviense	Passau	Petri	762	
	Miss. Remense	Paris	Dupré	827	
	Miss. Romanum	Venice	Novimagius	915	no. 144
	Miss. Romanum	Pavia	Girardengus	916	no. 145
	Miss. Romanum	Venice	Hamman	917	
	Miss. Romanum	Nuremberg	Fratres Eremiti	918	no. 146
	Miss. Romanum	Lyons	Trechsel	919	
	Miss. Rothomagense	Paris	Dupré	1342	
	Miss. Strigonense	Brünn	Stahel, &c.	1494	
	Miss. Virdunense	Paris	Dupré	1637	
	Miss. Vratislaviense	Strasbourg	Schott	1656	
	Miss. Xantonense	Paris	Higman	1663	no. 206
	Obsequiale	Nuremberg	Stuchs	751	no. 226
	Psalterium Ultraject.	Antwerp	Leeu	982	p. 40
	Psalterium	Milan	Pachel	924	
	Psalterium	Venice	s. typ.	978	
	Vigiliae Augustenses	Augsburg	Ratdolt	1090	no. 255
	Vigiliae Colonienses	Augsburg	Ratdolt	1092	
not after 1492	Psalterium	Lübeck	Ghotan	858	
c. 1492	Psalterium	Magdeburg	M. Brandis	862	
1492	Directorium	Mainz	Friedberg	579	p. 5
	Hymni	Paris	Caillaut	713	p. 7
	Miss. Andegavense	Paris	Hodian, &c.	56	
	Miss. Claramontense	Venice	Birreta	277	no. 58
	Miss. Ebroicense	Paris	Dupré	365	no. 66
	Miss. Frisingense	Augsburg	Ratdolt	396	no. 70
	Miss. Gnesnense	Mainz	Schoeffer	407/8	
	Miss. Meldense	Paris	Dupré	581	
	Miss. Parisiense	Paris	Gering	705	
	Miss. Ratisponense	Bamberg	Petzensteiner, &c.	807	no. 111
	Miss. Ratisponense	Bamberg	Sensenschmidt	808	no. 112
	Miss. Redonense	Paris	Hodian, &c.	818	no. 116
	Miss. Romanum	Milan	Zarotus	920	no. 147
	Miss. Romanum	s.l.	s. typ.	921	no. 148
	Miss. Romanum	Brescia	Britannicis	922	no. 149
	Miss. Romanum	Rome	Planck	923	
	Miss. Saltzburgense	Nuremberg	Stuchs	1378	no. 175
	Miss. Sarum	Rouen	Morin	1389	no. 178
	Miss. Trecense	Paris	Petit	1561	
	Miss. Valentinum	Venice	Hamman	1616	
	Miss. Virdunense	s.l.	s. typ.	1638	
	Ordinarium	Cologne	Renschen	767	p. 37

Date	Title	Place and Printer		Weale–Bohatta no.	This list
1492	Sequentiae	Deventer	Breda	1064	
c. 1493	Psalterium	Zinna	Monasterium Cisterc.	—	p. 46
	Psalterium	Cluny	Wenssler	953	
1493	Compendium	Mâcon	Wenssler	563	p. 4
	Graduale	Lübeck	Arndes	705	no. 19
	Miss. Bituricense	Paris	Higman	187	
	Miss. Brixinense	Augsburg	Ratdolt	206	no. 50
	Miss. Cluniacense	Cluny	Wenssler	1792	p. 33
	Miss. Eduense	Paris	Higman	375	no. 68
	Miss. Herbipolense	Würzburg	Reyser	433	no. 78
	Miss. Laudunense	Lausanne	Belot	491	no. 81
	Miss. Magdeburgense	Magdeburg	M. Brandis	572/572a	p. 16
	Miss. Moguntinum	Mainz	Schoeffer	626	no. 88
	Miss. Praedicatorum	Venice	Hamman	1821	
	Miss. Raceburgense	Nuremberg	Koberger	805	
	Miss. Romanum	Venice	Spira	924	no. 150
	Miss. Romanum	Venice	Hamman	925	no. 151
	Miss. Romanum	Venice	Hamman	926	no. 152
	Miss. Speciale	Strasbourg	Grüninger	1468	p. 29
	Miss. Tullense	Paris	Le Rouge	1584	no. 198
	Miss. Turonense	Rouen	Morin	1595	no. 199
	Obsequiale	Augsburg	Ratdolt	750	p. 35
	Processionale	Venice	Spira	—	no. 232
c. 1494	Directorium Moguntinum	Cologne	Quentell	581	p. 5
	Directorium Moguntinum	Mainz	Friedberg	580	p. 5
	Miss. Claramontense	Lyons	Topié	—	no. 59
	Psalterium	Leipzig	Kachelofen	854	
1494	Graduale	Augsburg	Ratdolt	703	no. 17
	Litanie	Milan	Zarotus	—	p. 7
	Manuale Constantiense	Rouen	Bourgeois	730	no. 27
	Manuale Toletanum	Seville	Comp. Alemanes	—	
	Manuale Hispalense	Seville	Ungut, &c.	731	p. 8
	Miss. Ambrosianum	Milan	de Meregariis, &c.	32	
	Miss. Aquilense	Augsburg	Ratdolt	79	no. 38
	Miss. Auriense	Monterey	la Passera, &c.	118	
	Miss. Basiliense	Basle	Wenssler	159	p. 11
	Miss. Brandenburgense	Nuremberg	Stuchs	199	
	Miss. Cenomanense	Paris	Higman	260	no. 57
	Miss. Coloniense	Cologne	Quentell	289	no. 62
	Miss. Eystettense	Eichstädt	Reyser	390	
	Miss. Lundense	s.l.	s. typ.	564	
	Miss. Pataviense	Augsburg	Ratdolt	763/4	no. 106
	Miss. Praedicatorum	Venice	Hamman	1822	no. 215
	Miss. Romanum	Venice	Pincius	927	
	Miss. Romanum	Naples	de Bantono	928	
	Miss. Romanum	Venice	Spira	929	no. 153
	Miss. Romanum	Rome	Planck	930	
	Miss. Romanum (slavonice)	Zengg	Mišti, &c.	1331	
	Miss. Sarum	Venice	Hamman	1390	no. 179

Date	Title	Place and Printer		Weale–Bohatta no.	This list
1494	Miss. Sarum	Venice	Hamman	1391	no. 180
	Miss. Strigonense	Venice	Hamman	1495	
	Miss. Treverense	s.l.	s. typ.	1576	
	Processionarium	Seville	Ungut, &c.	781	no. 233
	Processionarium	Venice	Spira	782	no. 235
	Psalterium	Deventer	Breda	925	p. 40
	Psalterium	Nuremberg	Koberger	—	p. 43
	Psalterium	Paris	Gering, &c.	962	no. 248
	Rituale Constantiense	s.l.	s. typ.	1049	
	Sequentiae	Deventer	Breda	1065	
	Sequentiae	Gouda	Collacie Broeders	1066	
c. 1495	Agenda Spirensis	Speyer	Drach	20	
	Ceremoniale Brixinense	Augsburg	Ratdolt	745?	no. 14
	Manuale Nannetense	Paris	Le Blanc	—	no. 28
	Miss. Halberstadtense			418	see c. 1500
	Miss. Leodiense	Delft	Snellaert	510	no. 85
	Obsequiale Brixinense				see Ceremoniale
	Psalterium Constantiense	s.l.	s. typ.	956	
	Psalterium	Paris	Jehannot	—	p. 43
	Psalterium	Strasbourg	Rusch	825 and 828	p. 44
	Psalterium	Strasbourg	Pruess	826?	no. 250
1495	Agenda brevis	Venice	Hamman	2	
	Agenda Pataviense	Venice	Hamman	17 (= 2?)	
	Antiphonarium	Augsburg	Ratdolt	23	no. 9
	Benedictionale Brixinense	Augsburg	Ratdolt	29	
	Directorium Augustense	Augsburg	Baemler	572	p. 4
	Directorium Sarum	Westminster	de Worde	586	p. 5
	Liber catechumeni	Venice	Spira	724	
	Miss. Auscitanum	Pavia	Girardengus	120	
	Miss. Cameracense	Paris	Higman	226	no. 53
	Miss. Eremitarum	Augsburg	Ratdolt	1811	no. 210
	Miss. Herbipolense	Würzburg	Reyser	434	p. 15
	Miss. Misnense	Leipzig	Kachelofen	610	
	Miss. Romanum	Venice	Pincius	931	no. 154
	Miss. Romanum	Lyons	Maréchal, &c.	932	
	Miss. Rothomagense	Rouen	Morin	1343	no. 171
	Miss. Strigonense	Venice	Hamman	1496	
	Miss. Ucetiense	Lyons	Numeister, &c.	1605	no. 201
	Ordinarium Bisuntinense	Paris	s. typ.	757	
	Psalterium	Venice	Tortis?	926	p. 45
	Psalterium	Nuremberg	Koberger		see 1494
before 1496	Processionarium	Paris	Toulouze	780	
c. 1496	Directorium Constantiense	s.l.	s. typ.	576	p. 4
	Psalterium	Venice	Spira	927	p. 45
	Rituale Romanum	Florence	de Emporio	1054	
	Sequentiae	Deventer	Pafraet	1067	
1496	Antiphonarium	Würzburg	Reyser	24	
	Compendium	Paris	Dupré	—	p. 4
	Graduale	Würzburg	Reyser	698	

Date	Title	Place and Printer		Weale–Bohatta no.	This list
1496	Liber catechumeni	Florence	Alopa	—	p. 7
	Manuale Bracarense	Monterey	Gherlinc	727	
	Miss. Augustense	Augsburg	Ratdolt	105	no. 40
	Miss. Herbipolense	Würzburg	Reyser	435	
	Miss. Parisiense	Paris	Morand	706	no. 103
	Miss. Parisiense	Paris	Dupré	707	
	Miss. Praedicatorum	Venice	Torresanus	1823	no. 216
	Miss Romanum	Venice	Spira	933	
	Miss. Romanum	Rome	Planck	934/5	no. 155
	Miss. Romanum	Lisbon	Moravus	—	p. 25
	Miss. Sagiense	Rouen	Morin	1372	p. 27
	Miss. Vicense	Barcelona	Rosenbach, &c.	1630	
	Obsequiale Saltzburgense	Nuremberg	Stuchs	752	no. 227
	Ordinarium Strigonense	Nuremberg	Stuchs	774	
	Psalterium	Louvain	Westfalia	968	
	Psalterium	Venice	Hamman	928	p. 45
	Psalterium	Venice	Spira	979	p. 45
	Rituale Pragense	Nuremberg	Stuchs	1050	
	Rituale Saltzburgense	Nuremberg	Stuchs	1055	
c. 1497	Ordinarium Cisterciense	Paris	Pigouchet	—	p. 37
	Vigiliae	Paris	Vérard	—	p. 47
1497	Agenda	Magdeburg	M. Brandis	10	no. 4
	Directorium Augustense	Augsburg	Ratdolt	573	p. 4
	Directorium Saltzburgense	Nuremberg	Stuchs	583	p. 5
	Hymnarium	Basle	Furter	716	
	Directorium Sarum	London	Pynson	587	p. 5
	Manuale Burgense	Zaragossa	Hurus	—	p. 7
	Manuale Parisiense	Paris	Morand	735	no. 29
	Miss. Bisuntinense	Paris	Dupré	175	no. 48
	Miss. Curiense	Augsburg	Ratdolt	349	
	Miss. Ebroicense	Rouen	Morin	366	no. 67
	Miss. Gratianopolitanum	Grenoble	Belot	413	
	Miss. Herbipolense	Würzburg	Reyser	436	
	Miss. Magdeburgense	Magdeburg	M. Brandis	573	p. 17
	Miss. Meldense	s.l.	s. typ.	582	
	Miss. Moguntinum	Speyer	Drach	627	no. 89
	Miss. Parisiense	Paris	Gering, &c.	708	no. 104
	Miss. Parisiense	Paris	Dupré	709	
	Miss. Pragense	Leipzig	Kachelofen	797	
	Miss. Praedicatorum	Venice	Bevilaqua	1824	no. 217
	Miss. Ratisponense	Bamberg	Pfeyl	810	no. 113
	Miss. Romanum	Lyons	Topié	936	
	Miss. Romanum	Venice	Torresanus	937	
	Miss. Romanum	Venice	Hamman	938	no. 156
	Miss. Romanum	Venice	Sessa	939	no. 157
	Miss. Romanum	Lyons	Maréchal, &c.	940	
	Miss. Romanum	Venice	Spira	941	no. 158
	Miss. Romanum	Venice	Bevilaqua	942	no. 159
	Miss. Sarum	Rouen	Morin	1392/3	nos. 181/2
	Miss. Sarum	Paris	Gering	1394	no. 183

Date	Title	Place and Printer		Weale–Bohatta no.	This list
1497	Miss. Trajectense	Paris	Higman, &c.	1554	no. 194
	Miss. Trecense	Paris	Dupré	1562	
	Miss. Warmiense	Strasbourg	Rusch	1646	
	Obsequiale Saltzburg.	Augsburg	Ratdolt	753	
	Pontificale	Rome	Planck	778	no. 230
	Psalterium	Ferrara	Laurentius	—	p. 41
	Psalterium	Leipzig	Kachelofen	929/30	p. 41
	Psalterium	Lübeck	Arndes	931	
	Psalterium	Lyons	Maréchal, &c.	932	
	Psalterium	Nuremberg	Hochfeder	933	p. 43
	Psalterium	Nuremberg	Koberger	—	p. 43
	Psalterium	Paris	Kerver	—	p. 44
	Psalterium	Venice	Girardengus	934	
	Psalterium	Venice	Hamman	980, 928?	
	Sequentiae	Basle	Furter	1068	
before 1498	Manuale Sarum	Paris	Gering	737	
	Miss. Romanum	Venice	Sessa	943	no. 160
	Psalterium	Strasbourg	Pruess	—	no. 250
c. 1498	Hymnarium	Paris	Vérard	712	see 1487
	Manuale Sarum	Rouen	s. typ.	739	
	Miss. Carthusiense	Speyer	Drach	1728	p. 33
	Miss. Speciale	Strasbourg	Grüninger	1469	p. 29
1498	Agenda Pataviensis	Venice	Hamman	18	no. 7
	Agenda Olomucensis	Nuremberg	Stuchs	15	
	Directorium	London	Pynson	588 (587?)	
	Hymni	Tarragona	Rosenbach	717	p. 7
	Liber catechumeni	Venice	Sessa	725	
	Miss. Ambianense	Paris	Dupré	13	
	Miss. Barcinonense	Barcelona	de Gumiel	150	
	Miss. Bellovacense	Paris	Dupré	165	
	Miss. Bursfeldense	Speyer	Drach	1681	no. 208
	Miss. Bracarense	Lisbon	Saxonia	196	no. 49
	Miss. Caesar-augustanum	Zaragossa	Hurus	219	
	Miss. Coloniense	Cologne	Bungart	290	no. 63
	Miss. Gebennense	Geneva	Belot	402	
	Miss. Pataviense	Augsburg	Ratdolt	765	
	Miss. Pictaviense	Paris	Higman	782	no. 107
	Miss. Pragense	Leipzig	Kachelofen	798	no. 109
	Miss. Pragense	Nuremberg	Stuchs	799	
	Miss. Romanum	Venice	Paganinis	944	
	Miss. Romanum	Venice	Spira	945	no. 162
	Miss. Romanum	Venice	Spira	946	no. 163
	Miss. Romanum	Venice	Sessa	947	
	Miss. Rothomagense	Rouen	Morin	—	see 1499
	Miss. Saltzburgense	Nuremberg	Stuchs	1379	no. 176
	Miss. Sarum	Westminster	Notary, &c.	1395	no. 184
	Miss. Speciale	Strasbourg	Grüninger	1470	
	Miss. Spirense	s.l.	s. typ.	1483	
	Miss. Strigonense	Nuremberg	Stuchs	1497	
	Miss. Strigonense	Venice	Spira	1498	no. 189
	Miss. Tornacense	Paris	Higman	1546 (= 1547?)	no. 193
	Miss. Treverense	Cologne	Quentell	1577	
	Ordinarium	Bologna	Rugiero	758	
	Psalterium	Antwerp	Back	935	

Chronological List

Date	Title	Place and Printer		Weale–Bohatta no.	This list
1498	Psalterium	Cologne	s. typ.	936	
	Psalterium	Leipzig	Lotter	937	
c. 1499	Antiphonarium	Venice	Spira	27	no. 11
	Miss. Bened. Mellicense	Nuremberg	Stuchs	1703	p. 32
	Ordinarium	Tarragona	Rosenbach	775	
1499	Agenda Vratislavensis	Strasbourg	Rusch	22	
	Graduale	Venice	Spira	704	no. 20
	Miss. Ambrosianum	Milan	Pachel	33	no. 36
	Miss. Bambergense	Bamberg	Pfeyl	132	no. 43
	Miss. Benedictinum	Montserrat	Luschner	1693	
	Miss. Constantiense	Rouen	Le Bourgeois	314	
	Miss. Dyense	Paris	Dupré	352	
	Miss. Giennense	Seville	Ungut	406	no. 72
	Miss. Herbipolense	Würzburg	Reyser	437	
	Miss. Hildensemense	Nuremberg	Stuchs	447	no. 79
	Miss. Itinerantium	Cologne	de Werden	459	p. 15
	Miss. Leodiense	Paris	Higman	511	no. 85
	Miss. Misnense	Speyer	Drach	612	
	Miss. Olomucense	Nuremberg	Stuchs	689	no. 95
	Miss. Quinque Ecclesiense	Venice	Paep	804	
	Miss. Romanum	Venice	Paganinis, &c.	948	
	Miss. Romanum	Milan	Pachel	949	no. 164
	Miss. Romanum	Venice	Arrivabene	950	no. 165
	Miss. Romanum	Lyons	Maréchal, &c.	951	no. 166
	Miss. Romanum	Venice	s. typ.	952	
	Miss. Rothomagense	Rouen	Morin	1344	no. 172
	Miss. Tarraconense	Tarragona	Rosenbach	1527	no. 192
	Miss. Teutonicorum	Nuremberg	Stuchs	1936	p. 34
	Miss. Toletanum	Toledo	Hagenbach	1536	
	Miss. Vapincense	s.l.	s. typ.	1619	
	Miss. Vratislaviense	Mainz	Schoeffer	1657/8	p. 32
	Obsequiale	Augsburg	Ratdolt	744	no. 224
	Psalterium	Antwerp	Liesvelt	938	
	Psalterium	Cologne	Bungart	939	
	Psalterium	Venice	Spira	—	p. 45
	Psalterium	Westminster	de Worde	940	
c. 1500	Agenda	Strasbourg	Pruess	4	p. 1
	Manuale Carthusiense	Rome?	Silber?	729	
	Manuale Divinum	Venice	Vitalibus	—	p. 8
	Miss. Halberstadtense	Strasbourg	Grüninger	418	no. 74
	Miss. Romanum	Venice	Pincius	953?	no. 167
	Miss. Romanum	s.l.	s. typ.	954	no. 168
	Miss. Speciale	Strasbourg	Pruess	1471	p. 29
	Psalterium	Antwerp	Eckert	—	p. 39
	Psalterium	Cologne	Quentell	841	p. 40
	Psalterium	Leipzig	Lotter	855	
1500	Antiphonarium, see Responsoriale				
	Graduale	Speyer	Drach	—	no. 18
	Directorium	Montserrat	Luschner	718	
	Liber catechumeni	Venice	Spira	726	no. 23
	Manuale Laudunense	Paris	Rubeus	732	
	Manuale Lausannense	Geneva	Belot	733	p. 8
	Manuale Carnotense	Paris	Higman	—	no. 25
	Manuale Rothomagense	Rouen	Morin, &c.	736	
	Manuale Sennonense	Paris	Hopyl	741	no. 30
	Manuale Sarum	Rouen	Olivier	740	(= 1501)

Date	Title	Place and Printer		Weale–Bohatta no.	This list
1500	Miss. Abulense	Salamanca	de Albornez (Porres)	5	
	Miss. Bisuntinense	Venice	Malietus	176	
	Miss. Bituricense	s.l.	s. typ.	188	
	Miss. Cabilonense	Lyons	Boninis	213	no. 51
	Miss. Carmelitorum	Venice	Giunta	1885	no. 220
	Miss. Itinerantium	Cologne	Quentell	460	p. 16
	Miss. Laudunense	s.l.	s. typ.	484	
	Miss. Lausannense	Geneva	Belot	492	p. 16
	Miss. Lemovicense	Limoges	Berton	498	no. 83
	Miss. Leodiense	Speyer	Drach	512	
	Miss. Lugdunense	Lyons	Ungarus	548	
	Miss. Misnense	Leipzig	Kachelofen	613	
	Miss. Mozarabicum	Toledo	Hagenbach	654	no. 93
	Miss. Praedicatorum	Venice	Spira	1825	no. 218
	Miss. Praedicatorum	Venice	Giunta	1826	
	Miss. Ratisponense	Bamberg	Pfeyl	811	no. 114
	Miss. Redonense	Rouen	Mauditier	819	p. 20
	Miss. Romanum	Lyons	Sachon	955/6	nos. 169/70
	Miss. Romanum	Venice	s. typ.	957	
	Miss. Romanum	Venice	Spira	958	
	Miss. Romanum	Venice	Bevilaqua	959	
	Miss. Sagiense	Rouen	Regnault	1373	no. 174
	Miss. Sarum	Paris	Higman	1396	no. 185
	Miss. Sarum	Paris	Dupré	1397	
	Miss. Sarum	London	Pynson	1398	no. 186
	Miss. Segoviense	Venice	Spira	1455	
	Miss. Spirense	Speyer	Drach	1484	
	Miss. Strigonense	Venice	Paep	1499	no. 190
	Miss. Trecense	Paris	Dupré	1563	no. 196
	Miss. Turonense	s.l.	s. typ.	1596	no. 200
	Ordinarium Turonense	Paris	Levet	776	p. 38
	Ordinarium Praemonstratense	s.l.	s. typ.	768	p. 37
	Processionarium	Montserrat	Luschner	779	no. 231
	Psalterium	s.l.	s. typ.	941 = 926?	
	Psalterium	Magdeburg	M. Brandis	942	
	Psalterium Constantiense	Mainz	s. typ.	958	no. 244
	Psalterium	Paris	de la Barre, &c.	943	p. 44
	Psalterium	Venice	s. typ.	879	
	Responsoriale	Montserrat	Luschner		no. 253
	Rituale Ucetiense	Lyons	s. typ.	1056	
	Sequentiae	Cologne	Quentell	1069	

INDEX OF PRINTERS

THIS and the following Index of Places include numbered items in this catalogue only. An asterisk with the number indicates that the book has actual printed music and notes.

INDEX OF PLACES

PRINTED IN GREAT BRITAIN
AT THE UNIVERSITY PRESS, OXFORD
BY VIVIAN RIDLER
PRINTER TO THE UNIVERSITY